FITNESS PROFESSIONALS

THE PERSONAL TRAINER'S HANDBOOK

EBECCA WEISSBORT

manage your business • know your clients

A & C BLACK • LONDON

Thanks to Fitness Professionals Ltd (www.fitpro.com) for supporting the Fitness Professionals series.

Note

While every effort has been made to ensure that the content of this book is as technically accurate and as sound as possible, neither the author nor the publisher can accept responsibility for any injury or loss sustained as a result of the use of this material.

Published in 2006 by A & C Black Publishers Ltd
38 Soho Square, London W1D 3HB
www.acblack.com

ISBN-10: 0-7136-7557-8
ISBN-13: 978-0-7136-7557-3

A CIP catalogue record for this book is available from the British Library.

Typeset in 10½ on 12pt Baskerville BE Regular by Palimpsest Book Production Limited, Polmont, Stirlingshire

A & C Black uses paper produced with elemental chlorine-free pulp, harvested from managed sustainable forests.

Acknowledgements
Cover photograph © Getty Images
Illustration on page 23 by Jean Ashley

Printed and bound in Great Britain by Biddles Ltd, Guildford and Kings Lynn.

CONTENTS

ACKNOWLEDGEMENTS

There are many people who contributed to this book and some people who showed immense generosity in offering their time and knowledge. I would like to offer my gratitude to the following people: Steve Jack for his belief that there is always enough to go round and for sharing his expertise; Cliff Collins at REPs; Julia Miles for her friendship, support and input; Rob Brown; Cyril Cooper for stepping in when I had just about given up on the insurance business; Tony Whittle for always being there for me and for his invaluable expertise in marketing; Dad and Valentina for their support and for telling me 'how to write a book' – everything you said was right! Thanks also to A & C Black for making this happen – to Julia Stanton for an outstanding idea and to Rob and Claire for being so great to work with.

This project would definitely not have got off the ground had it not been for some key people. Thank you to my friend John McAdam for asking the right question at the right time and to Wendy Mandy for working her magic on me. Thank you most of all to Brian for believing in me when I doubted myself and for being there through thick and thin! You truly are an amazing person and I am privileged to share my life with you.

INTRODUCTION

Welcome to the first British personal trainer manual! You may notice that it is not like other manuals you have seen before – this is because we are not the same as the rest of the world and so I have included in this book information that is specific to the UK population and culture. You will also notice that this is not a textbook in the most traditional sense: I have not included much information about physiology, training methodologies, what exercises to do and how to perform a fitness assessment. This is because if you are not yet a personal trainer but are exploring the possibility of being one, you don't need that kind of information yet and, if you are already a personal trainer, you will be able to find it in your course materials and in other specific texts.

Instead, this book is designed to signpost you where to go next. I have covered a lot of topics and focused on the business of personal training. I truly believe that if we focus our attention on the technical expertise needed to train clients without balancing it by working on the other vital elements of training, such as business and interpersonal skills, then we are missing half the story. My aim in this book is therefore to emphasise the 'people' side of our work as much as the technical so that you have all the tools you need to create and build a phenomenal business.

I love this industry and I have watched it grow and develop so much over the last few years. I have been a gym and class instructor, personal trainer, GP Referral specialist, manager, speaker, trainer and writer. In all these roles I have been and continue to be inspired by the people in our business. In writing this book I hope that the experience I have gained in over 15 years in this industry and in business is useful to you. I wish I had known back then when I started what I know now!

Rebecca Weissbort
February 2006

PART ONE

BEING A PERSONAL TRAINER

WHY BE A PERSONAL TRAINER? 1

In this chapter you will:

- discover the qualities needed to become a personal trainer
- debunk the myths about being a personal trainer
- find out the difference between a gym instructor and a personal trainer.

So you want to be a personal trainer?

Feeling fit and fabulous, I roll up at my client's house in my new Porsche. Peter is a stockbroker who lives in a seven-bedroom house in Surrey. He opens the door, dressed and ready to go. We set off for our run and chat about what he's been up to over the past week. When we return, I make sure he's stretched out, then we go through to the kitchen to talk about his diet regime and how he's getting on. He then hands me a cheque for next month's sessions. I train him twice a week. My next client happens to be his next-door neighbour, Sheryl. Sheryl is a new mum who has a small home gym, so we work indoors. She's great fun and always has a funny story to tell. From there, just two more clients before I go home to pack. My celebrity client (you know who!) has asked me to go away with him to LA where he is shooting his latest film. I have trained him for seven years and he trusts me implicitly. He wants me to be on call to train him for roughly an hour a day. The rest of the time is my own. I will be away for about two weeks…

… in my dreams! Being a personal trainer is a very attractive prospect for lots of people. It has a glamorous image and a certain amount of status, you get to pick your own working hours and you are not stuck in an office five days a week. The perception is that you can earn a lot of money as well. Well, bits of that are true or can be true, but it is important that you get real about what it takes to be a personal trainer and what it can be like. For a start, it is possible to earn big money, but a lot of personal trainers struggle financially and finally give up and go back to being employed. Also, while the hourly rate might seem attractive, you need to take into account all the other costs associated with your business, such as equipment, professional memberships, kit, insurance, travel, training, advertising and so on. In addition, just how many hours per day can you work? Being a personal trainer is taxing on your body and can be mentally draining. If you work outside of a gym setting, you also need to take travel time into consideration. So, when all is said and done, the average hourly rate is not as high as it first seems.

Picking your own hours seems like the ideal way to work, but you must remember that most of your clients will want your services in the early morning or the evening, Monday to Friday. This effectively means working in two shifts. Again, you need to think about how this will fit into your personal life and also how your personal life affects your energy levels. You must be prepared to put in the time to build your business and work unsociable hours, at least until you are established.

In reality, being a personal trainer is not a

glamorous profession and, if glamour is what you are attracted to, personal training may not be the career for you. The hours are long: in addition to training clients, you also need to spend time planning and working on notes for each client, marketing, managing your finances and so on. You'll be running around, lugging great loads of equipment from car to various locations, listening to your clients' problems – it's just not that glam! It can also be a rather isolating profession.

On the flip side of all of this, there are those trainers who manage to hit the high end of the scale and charge very highly for their services. While money isn't everything, it is possible to make a lot of money if you really focus on it. You may also be lucky enough to work in an environment or tap into a market where you can work largely daytime hours. Again, that is the exception, but there are trainers out there doing just that.

So, if you want a job where you can be your own boss, you get to meet great people, you are part of a vibrant and exciting industry, you get to make a difference in people's lives, you are constantly learning and you get to indulge your fascination with fitness and wellness, then personal training is the job for you.

Qualities of a personal trainer

A good personal trainer has to have many different skills and personal qualities. Of course, everyone has their own style of working and every client you encounter will want something different, but the profile of a good personal trainer will probably include some of the following attributes:

- being fit and interested in your own personal fitness
- organisation
- a customer-focused attitude
- being friendly and open
- enjoying working with people
- being a leader
- being positive and encouraging
- having empathy for your clients
- being able to wear different hats: trainer, marketing person, sales person, book keeper and administrator
- strong communication skills
- confidence
- being able to work alone.

This list is by no means exhaustive and you may well have other ideas, interests and skills that would be good in a personal training context. However, thinking about the general skills involved with being a personal trainer will help you to assess if this is a good career choice for you.

Fitness instructor or personal trainer?

There appears to be a lot of confusion around this. The general public often don't know the difference, many gyms use Level 2 gym instructors (the basic qualification, see Chapter 2) as 'personal trainers' and many people trying to become personal trainers for the first time are confused as well. What, then, is the difference between a personal trainer and a fitness instructor?

A **gym instructor** is trained to teach safely within a gym setting. They can write general programmes for apparently healthy adults and supervise people to use a gym safely. However, they are not competent to work with any special populations such as older adults or clients with specific medical conditions, and can only offer the most general programmes;

the training at Level 2 precludes more advanced programming, so gym instructors will find themselves limited in the kind of programmes they are able to offer and the depth at which they can work. Relationships with clients will therefore be of a much more superficial nature. The job description of a gym instructor also differs from that of a personal trainer in that the former would be expected to clean equipment and carry out other broad-spectrum activities such as administrative duties within the gym setting.

In comparison, a **personal trainer** can individualise programmes to a much greater extent and respond rapidly to changing circumstances. Personal trainers should be trained to Level 3 (see page 8) and are marked out by their skills in fitness assessment, exercise programming, diet and weight management knowledge, injury prevention and rehabilitation, specialist skills and in-depth knowledge of pre- and post-natal exercise, seniors and clients with medical conditions. They should offer a higher level of service and be able to interact with clients particularly well. Table 1.1 outlines the key differences between gym instructors and personal trainers.

This book is aimed at those considering personal training as a career choice, existing gym instructors who would like to take themselves to the next level and qualified personal trainers who are looking for a reference book. For the latter group, this book should provide revision and also act as a signpost to where you might go for specific help.

Table 1.1 Comparison of skills of gym instructors and personal trainers

Gym instructor	*Personal trainer*
• Able to work on the gym floor, offering encouragement and helping customers to exercise effectively and safely • Able to design and teach gym programmes to apparently healthy adults • Able to carry out gym inductions for new users.	• Able to carry out fitness assessments and lifestyle audits • Possesses advanced skills in exercise training and has a greater ability to adapt programmes as necessary • Able to offer nutritional advice and weight management as a service to clients • Able to work with special populations such as older adults, pre-/post-natal, sports conditioning and medical conditions • Possesses an understanding of psychological tools and is able to use these to promote behaviour change and increase client motivation.

GETTING QUALIFIED AND STAYING THAT WAY

In this chapter you will:

- discover the standards needed to become a personal trainer in the UK
- learn how to choose the best training provider for you
- discover what continued professional development is and how it applies to you.

You will need to acquire many skills in your quest to become a personal trainer and, once you are qualified, you will need to continue adding to your skills and knowledge base. This may mean sharpening up some 'soft' skills as well as learning new, more advanced training techniques and specialisms; in other words, aside from your technical knowledge of training you will also need to learn about exercise counselling, health screening, exercise adherence, marketing and customer care, to name a few. These are all fundamental skills for your business and you will need to be committed to continued learning in order to keep yourself up to date and ahead of the game.

How do I get qualified?

There is no easy answer to this question. In the UK the industry has been largely unregulated, which means that anyone can set themselves up as a personal trainer any time they wish. For those who want to do more than cheat clients out of their valuable time and money, the vast array of qualifications can be baffling.

In many other industries, especially those that entail dealing with people's health, there is a professional body and, without membership of that body, an individual cannot practise. Think, for example, about doctors (British Medical Association), physiotherapists (Chartered Society of Physiotherapy) and dentists (British Dental Association), to name a few. Although it is not governed by British law, the personal training industry does now have an organisation that offers a system of self-regulation. The Register of Exercise Professionals (REPs) was designed to bring clarity to the whole situation and to offer the public reassurance as to the kind of qualifications they should be looking for in an exercise professional. Membership is down to the individual, but more and more employers in the fitness industry are requesting membership as part of their employment terms and REPs is increasingly recognised outside the fitness industry as well. The Department of Health, for example, has advised all clinicians to refer patients only to fitness professionals who appear on the Register (Medical Defence Union advice to members, 2005).

By necessity, REPs is an independent organisation not affiliated to any training organisation. The Register is split into different levels of qualification, so it is completely clear what constitutes, for example, a fitness instructor, a group exercise instructor or a personal trainer. The system is aligned to UK National Occupational Standards (NOS), which means that all qualifications and certificates have to cover certain areas and ensures they are all up to the same standard. NOS either already exist or are in the process of being agreed for all UK work roles. They are approved by the Qualifications and Curriculum Authority

(QCA) and have been developed by employers and those representing a particular field or industry – in this case, exercise and fitness. NOS describe the standards that people are required to achieve in their work and specify the skills and knowledge that are needed to be able to perform that work effectively. This effectively brings all qualifications onto a level playing field because, no matter who the provider is, they have to arrive at the same standard to align themselves with the NOS.

In the fitness industry, the entry level is Level 2, which includes exercise to music and the basic gym certificate. Personal trainers need to achieve Level 3 (Advanced Instructor). This enables any client to assess a trainer's competence, regardless of what course they have done. At present, membership of the Register is voluntary, but there is increasing pressure for exercise professionals to conform as awareness of the Register grows. If you are looking to come into this profession, REPs is a great place to start in terms of getting advice and information. Members must commit to Continued Professional Development and also adhere to a Code of Ethical Practice.

There are several ways to get yourself qualified. The first is to take a basic level qualification such as exercise to music or gym instructor. You could then add on modules in fitness assessment, nutrition and weight management, stress management, applied exercise programming, exercise counselling, corrective exercise, GP referral, pre- and post-natal exercise, walking and so on. Doing a full qualification in modules allows you to gain valuable experience in the industry while you learn. Bear in mind that the new Level 3 Advanced Instructor qualification should be completed before working in more specialist areas; this is a pre-requisite. The REPs website (see page 143 for details) has a chart which shows the qualification structure.

Some of the larger health club chains offer a route into personal training via their own in-house training academies. Many of these are now recognised by REPs. Some will even take you as a complete beginner without any basic qualification. Bear in mind with this route that you will not be an independent trainer while you work for a company and that working and training in-house at a large organisation entails various advantages and disadvantages (see Table 2.1).

Find out the whole picture and make sure that is what you want before you sign up.

Another way in is the graduate route. If your degree is sports, leisure, exercise or health related, you will need to follow your degree by taking an exercise teaching qualification to give you the practical skills needed to be a personal trainer. You may be able to fast track your way through the various 'recognised' fitness qualifications to enable you to get on the Register or to be qualified sooner. This can be done through some of the training providers who offer a system of Accredited Prior Learning, which allows you to prove your knowledge without necessarily having to take an entire course. When looking for a training provider it is worth checking to see if they offer this service to students; it is actually quite rare, even though all approved centres should offer it.

Choosing your training provider

The number of courses being recognised by REPs is growing all the time and, for that reason, it is impossible to recommend one course over another. A list of current training providers is included in Appendix 2 (see pages 143–4), but it is always worth checking with REPs that the course you want to do does in fact give you the competence required and that

Table 2.1 Advantages and disadvantages of training in a gym setting

Advantages	*Disadvantages*
Provides a way of financing your training while working.	Wages may be low and the hours may be long and unsociable.
Gives you valuable industry experience.	You may be committed to working for that organisation for a set period of time or 'paying back' the cost of your training.
Everything is provided for you, saving you from shopping around for different courses and training providers and checking out their reputations within the industry.	You have no choice in what you learn and from whom and you may not be able to study at a pace that is right for you.
You have access to support and help from colleagues.	You could become very 'corporate' in your approach and develop a narrow view of the industry.
You will learn valuable skills in selling your personal training services and will be able to put these into practice.	Your approach to personal training may become very 'sales' driven, which can be a turn-off for some people.

it is recognised by REPs at the level you require. Your training represents a big investment of your time and money, so choose your course well and do your own research until you are happy with your choice. Remember that the easiest option may seem tempting, but you will have to deal with the results after you have finished your training and a course that is not recognised or not highly thought of will be to your disadvantage in the longer term.

Do not choose your course solely on price as there is a huge difference in terms of quality. Similarly, don't just do the quickest course, tempting though this may be. You need to make sure that:

- the course is recognised by REPs
- it covers everything you need in enough depth
- the company offers you support in the longer term
- you can learn at the pace that is right for you.

Get the brochures, talk to the training companies and speak to their graduates as well to find out how they found the course and how they found their general dealings with the company or organisation.

Most courses in the UK take anything from 12 weeks to one year to complete, depending on several factors, such as whether you want to study part or full time or whether you are a complete novice or already have some industry experience or qualifications.

Continued learning

The fitness industry and sport as a science are still very new and, as such, changes are happening all the time. Indeed, the breadth of courses available now even compared with just five years ago is huge, and all courses are under constant revision. New products and services appear all the time and it is important that you develop the technical expertise to deliver them. In addition to all of this, it is a condition of membership of REPs that you acquire Continued Professional Development in the style of a points system to be submitted annually.

There are many different ways to continue learning once you are certified and a myriad of different areas in which to study. See Chapter 9 for some ideas of areas you could specialise in.

Technical training

You could choose to specialise in a certain area of fitness and might therefore take courses in advanced instruction and your chosen area. This can be done via formal training providers, by attendance at conferences and workshops and by reading around your subject (REPs offer accreditation in all these ways, providing that the material studied has been approved by them). Specialised courses might include GP Referrals, which covers many different medical conditions, or something specific like Cardiac Rehab Phase IV, which is run by the British Association of Cardiac Rehab (see page 144 for contact details).

In addition to the huge variety of courses you can take, it is of course vital that you keep your CPR (cardio-pulmonary resuscitation) certificate up to date at all times. You will need this in order to qualify as a personal trainer anyway, but you must also re-take the exam every three years. Aside from the obvious reason of being able to respond in an emergency situation, it is also required for REPs membership and to keep your insurance valid. Many personal trainers also choose to do the full first-aid certificate. In many ways, this is probably more useful than just CPR as the incidents and emergencies you may encounter are likely to be more varied than needing to resuscitate an individual. The full first-aid certificate entails a four-day course and is again valid for three years. Your training provider may offer courses in first aid and CPR or you can contact St John Ambulance or the British Red Cross (see page 144 for contact details.

Soft skills

Soft skills such as customer care, rapport building, listening and counselling are often undervalued by personal trainers, which is reflected in the amount of time spent studying them. Arguably, though, they can be seen as far more important and profitable in the long run than hours spent studying more and more about the human body. The ability to communicate effectively and to run your business is crucial to your success. Many organisations offer training in these areas and it can be good to look outside of the fitness industry for ideas and courses. There are some great books, tapes, CDs and DVDs on the market, as well as courses. Conferences are useful and, even if you can't get to everything you want, sessions are sometimes recorded and available for purchase after the event.

PART TWO

RUNNING YOUR BUSINESS

STARTING UP

3

In this chapter you will:

- start to define your client group or specific market segment
- identify the advantages and disadvantages of different training settings
- learn what type of insurance you will need
- identify ways of handling the question of money with your clients
- learn how to organise your work and your office to operate at maximum efficiency
- learn what is involved in setting up your own gym.

Who are your clients?

Starting out as a personal trainer can be a daunting process. Obviously, the best way to get clients is by referral, but until you are known this is impossible. So the question is, where do you start? Where are your potential clients? Let's leave aside the gym environment to start with because within a gym there is a ready-made clientele, which brings with it its own challenges.

It helps enormously to think about who your clients are. There are numerous ways to narrow down your search for prospective clients – perhaps you have a particular interest or specialism, such as a particular sport, or maybe you have specific training that can help you in your search and make things significantly easier. For example, if you have played rugby to a high level and now have your personal training qualifications, you can combine the two and help rugby players work on specific fitness for their sport (we take it for granted that sports players know how to train for their sport, but that isn't always the case). Once you have this starting point, you will have more of a clue about where to find your clients; perhaps a sport-specific magazine or newsletter would carry an advert for your services, or perhaps there is a local club. Other areas of specialism include training clients with specific medical conditions or health issues (if you have trained in this area), older people, stressed-out executives or people wanting to lose weight. Whatever your specialism, make sure it is an area you are passionate about. Being passionate about a particular topic allows you to become obsessed by it, and this obsession or fascination is what will drive clients to you and what will drive you to become an expert in the field. Learn to live and breathe your chosen topic.

Even if you do not have a specific area of expertise, don't forget that your personal experience can be an invaluable source of inspiration when combined with your personal training skills. For example, if you are a parent you will understand the particular issues, barriers to exercise and challenges that parents must deal with in order to fit physical activity into a life that seems to be entirely based around family priorities; you will also understand the importance of looking after yourself so that you have the energy to meet those demands. If that is a market you wish to tap into, the obvious places to look for clients would be local schools or other places that parents attend, such as after-school clubs, parents' evenings, team events and park playgrounds. You will probably have your own network of potential clients right under your nose. And if you choose to go down this route, it would be a good idea to add on related skills to your repertoire, such as pre- and post-natal exercise.

Perhaps you want to go for a more general approach, but you want to narrow your business down to a particular geographical area. This makes sense in several ways: business-wise, you will spend less time travelling and more time earning; local people tend to know each other, so your reputation could spread quickly; and also, if you are seen working locally, your profile will be raised. A lot of people like to employ local people, and the community will soon recognise you and you will become known. That in itself is a great advert. Once you know an area, you will discover where the local people communicate with each other. For example, a coffee shop, library or deli might have a notice board. Perhaps there is a very vocal residents' association or a local trade directory. Then, once you have narrowed down to a particular area, you need to think about the following questions: what are the people like there? What is the culture? How do people dress? The more you can mould yourself to the profile of the people there, the more you will 'fit in' and be an obvious choice.

It is important to segment your market and decide what and who you are targeting. As mentioned above, you don't have to have a particular skill – sometimes our most obvious market, the one that would be perfect for us, is right under our noses and we don't even notice; for example, you might be a parent (as discussed above) or perhaps you have suffered from a specific medical condition and have become very knowledgeable in that area. In choosing your market segment, consider the following questions:

- Who are my current clients and do they have anything in common?
- Who do I want to work with?
- Do I have a particular interest?
- Do I want to specialise or have I specialised in a specific aspect of physical activity?
- What sort of person am I?

When you have narrowed down your choice, consider the following:

- What issues do this group of people face that could be a challenge to them when considering taking up an exercise programme?
- Does this client group have a particular style of dress or culture?
- Where will I find this client group?

Once you have defined your niche, the trick is to become a known 'expert' in it. Building that expertise can be done in several ways. The first and most obvious is to take courses and gain qualifications. This helps to prove your credentials. In addition to this, attending workshops and lectures and reading books and journals all help to increase your knowledge base. From there you have to get out there and market yourself. It is no use being an expert if no-one knows about you.

Case study

John had worked as an accountant for his entire career. At the age of 62, he was diagnosed with cancer. Following surgery and treatment, John found he had become unfit and had put on weight. He decided to start exercising and enlisted the help of a personal trainer. This proved to be so motivating and so successful in helping John to recover that he decided to retrain as a personal trainer himself. His surgeon, so impressed by the results of John's exercise regime, invited him to train other patients at his private clinic. John now specialises in pre- and post-operative cancer patients.

Where to find work

Many personal trainers are sole traders – that is, they work alone. However, it is possible to find work in gyms or to set up your own personal training studio where you start to build a bigger business and take on other trainers (see pages 26–31). It is also possible to get work through an agency.

Gyms

Many gyms will not allow personal trainers to work within their clubs unless they are authorised. It is vital that you find out what the situation is in the gym where you want to work. Trying to train your client surreptitiously, hoping that no one will notice, is not only potentially embarrassing for you and your client but is extremely bad practice and only brings the profession into disrepute.

Many health clubs and leisure centres now employ gym staff who double as personal trainers. Unless these trainers are qualified to personal trainer standards, be sure that the service being offered is not of the level it should be. If this is the situation, then unless you are prepared to work on the gym floor and get clients that way, move on. On the other hand, this can be a way in and a good personal trainer will build a busy and lucrative practice from talking to gym members and gaining visibility as a well-qualified professional. Some larger chains also offer full-time personal training positions. Other gyms charge a 'rent' to personal trainers who want to train their members. This means you will pay either a monthly fee that allows you to work in the centre, or a percentage of your client fees to the centre.

The advantages of working in a club setting are that you have access to a constant supply of potential clients, travel time is limited, it is safe and you have the added backup of club staff should an emergency occur. You have access to gym equipment, making programming straightforward and simple. You also have company.

The disadvantages are that some of your hard-earned cash has to be given up, competition between trainers for new clients can be fierce and, if you are the new trainer in an established club, getting started can be hard. In addition, client programming can be a little dull when it is solely based within a gym setting.

Other working environments

Local parks

Parks and open spaces can be great places to train, depending on the weather. They allow for creative programming and are free to use. In addition, local parks can be the hub of a community and your visibility in this setting could be a great advertisement for your business!

On the down side, some people do feel embarrassed about exercising in public and if the weather is awful you may need a contingency plan. You should always be ruled by your clients' wants and needs, while encouraging them to push past their comfort zone. In addition, your safety procedures will be quite different and you will need to give this some thought *before* you take clients outside.

Clients' homes

This is often the starting point for many personal trainers. Homes can be a good place for people who are short on time or do not have the confidence to work out in public. There are obviously things to take into consideration, such as space, ventilation and equipment. You may also find this a more isolating experience than, say, working within a gym setting. You might miss the camaraderie, but also the opportunities to confer with fellow professionals over any issues you may encounter. Your safety is also something that should not be taken for granted; make sure you refer to Chapter 5 for safety issues. However, you can charge more for working in clients' homes as people realise that they are paying for this convenience and that while you are travelling between homes you are unable to earn money.

Insurance

There is a perception that we have suddenly started to follow trends seen in the United States of America, with the belief that claims are huge and 'everyone is claiming'. The reality of the situation is that in the UK the number of claims is still very low and, even where there have been claims made against personal trainers, courts will rarely put the blame on one person. Most claims are far too complicated for that and therefore responsibility is usually shared. For this reason, the over-riding advice is that public liability insurance of £2 million is the minimum needed to practise as a personal trainer in the UK. This figure is historical. Local authorities required this amount of cover from instructors when the industry was still in its infancy and it has now been adopted as the industry standard by both the public and private sector. As long as you follow industry-based best practice and remain insured, you are doing as much as you can to protect yourself and your clients.

Confusion often arises when personal trainers assume that as they are working for just one company (i.e. they are not working alone and travelling to clients' houses) they are covered by that company's insurance. While this is sometimes the case, you must check this out for sure. If there is any doubt in your mind or you cannot get definitive information, then get your own insurance. There are a number of other things to consider as well. If you work for a company, you may only be insured as long as you train clients on the company's premises. As soon as you take clients off-site, you may not be covered. Also, check whether your insurance is based on when the claim arises: some insurers will cover you for any claim made in the future against you, but others will not. The other thing to consider if you work for a small company is that, should a claim arise and the company is in financial difficulties, they may not be able to pay out. In these instances it is prudent to have your own cover.

What types of insurance are available and what do I need?

Public liability insurance

Every personal trainer needs public liability insurance. It will cover you for bodily injury or for damage to property caused by you. It covers any event that occurs while you are with your client; an injury may occur afterwards, but if it is caused by something that happened in the time you were together you will be covered. It is important to check that your policy also covers you for professional indemnity, which will cover you for any advice you give. Another thing to consider when choosing your policy are the territorial limits of your insurance: some policies will only cover you for the UK, others extend to the EU, some are worldwide and some might cover worldwide except for the USA and Canada. Finally, public liability insurance will not cover you for any articles you may write and get published where the complainant is not a client. Ensure you think about your needs and check the small print accordingly.

Currently, the minimum level of cover is £2 million, although you can get cover for higher amounts.

Sports equipment insurance

This will cover any sports/fitness equipment you use. You will need to insure other equipment, such as computers, separately.

Personal accident insurance

This will cover you in the event of an accident at work. You need to think carefully about whether this is useful to you. It may be exactly what you want. However, most accidents do not happen at work – you know what you are doing in a gym and when you are training and are therefore unlikely to injure yourself in that setting. It may be better for you to look for 24-hour personal accident insurance. You will then be covered for any accident that occurs at any time, even when you're not at work. There are a couple of things to take into consideration with this type of insurance. First, make sure the insurance covers you for *your own* occupation and not *any* occupation: if you are injured but could do a desk job (but not personal training), some insurance policies will not cover you because technically you can still work. Second, you might prefer to ensure that your insurance covers you for illness as well as injury: personal accident only covers you for a sudden and unforeseen incident, but illness cover will additionally cover you if you have 'wear and tear' injuries. Again, check the small print and make sure you get exactly what you need.

The only thing to say about insurance is 'get it!' Most of your clients will ask for it and all professional organisations will require it before you become a member. More importantly, you may one day need it!

What should I look for in an insurance policy?

Always check that your insurance covers you for the purposes you require. In other words, if you have a business and your turnover is high and/or you employ other trainers, you may need a different insurance policy from a personal trainer who works alone; also consider whether you need employer's liability insurance. If you will be working abroad for any length of time, check that you will still be covered while you are out of the UK. Some insurers will cover you for a set period of time while abroad.

Where do I get insurance?

Many of the fitness organisations in the UK offer insurance in addition to their membership packages, so always check. Do not automatically take out the first policy offered to you, however. As with your training, make sure you shop around and compare policies before you buy.

Waivers and informed consent

Personal trainers seem to be rather attached to these and you will see waivers included in many other publications. However, I have chosen not to include them in this manual as they basically have no worth. The 1977 Act of Parliament, 'Unfair Contract Terms Act', explains that a contract between two unequal parties is not enforceable. What this means to you as a personal trainer is that, if you ask a client (the unequal party) to sign such a form, it will not be enforceable in law. You cannot sign away your responsibility or your duty of care as a trainer. The best you can do is to keep yourself insured, screen your clients well, keep your training updated and operate according to best practice. Keep good records of any advice you offer and any programmes you suggest for your client and remember to keep your clients' safety and well-being uppermost in your mind at all times.

Money

For most people, money is the reason we get up and go to work in the first place. For some people, dealing with money is easy; for others, it is really difficult to get hold of, manage and keep – but there is no doubt that most people have some kind of concern around the stuff! This section will give you an overview of some of the issues, but you may well find you need further advice and help, especially if this is the first time you have worked for yourself. A good accountant will be able to help you with this and the Inland Revenue can be very useful in helping you fill out your tax return.

Pricing yourself appropriately

Deciding what to charge can be a real minefield, especially if you are working alone. What is an appropriate price to charge for an hour of your time? Clearly, there will be a market average, but what makes it possible for one trainer to charge £100 while another feels they can only 'get away with' charging £25? There are many factors that will help you decide what to charge, including:

- experience
- qualifications
- location
- market forces
- self-confidence
- whether you have a specialism
- location of sessions and your costs
- size of current practice
- your personal financial needs.

It is vital that you do local research. Find out what other trainers in your area charge. Find out what other trainers offer in their sessions. In other words, is there any difference between the service they offer and the one you offer? Find out the difference between the service offered by the most expensive trainers and that offered by the cheapest. This will at least give you a feel for the market. However, there is no right way of going about this. Most personal trainers tend to start out as sole traders or as part-time trainers who also have another job. The only thing to take into account if you are a sole trader is that in order to make a living you will need to carry out several sessions every week, probably around 20. Never underestimate just how exhausting this can be. Many personal trainers start off with tons of enthusiasm and love their new career path, only to fail 18 months in because they just burn out. This is why your pricing system is so crucial.

One of the biggest issues when it comes to pricing is self-confidence. We all know that the most expensive is not necessarily the best, but when we are putting a price on our own time our confidence, or lack of, often gets in the way. What we are really saying is 'I'm only worth £x'. If this is you, then read Chapter 4 on marketing, get some clients and experience under your belt and work on your own confidence levels. As you (and your clients) get results, your confidence will start to grow. There's a surprising thing about money and wanting more of it: sometimes you only have to ask! Why is it that some people still get paid more than others for doing the same job? Why is it that some sales people in gyms do so much better than others at getting people to join? In almost every case, it comes down to asking! So many people are afraid to ask for money. We make huge presumptions about attitudes to money and assume that everyone feels the same way we do. If you were to ask 100 people about their attitude to money, you would be amazed at the response. For some people, the decision to purchase a gym membership is easy. A £200 joining fee? No problem. For others, the prospect of signing up for a year's membership, even at a much lower rate, might send them screaming to the hills! Everyone is different, but if you don't ask, you don't get. So, get over your fear of money (if you have one) and get used to stating your fees and explaining your payment terms as simply and easily as you can – with no apologies!

Case study

Anna Beale, a young consultant, was in her first year of business. She was quite overwhelmed with work, albeit not as well paid as she liked, but things were going well for someone so early on in their self-employed career. One day, she got a phone call from an ex-employer. He was looking for someone to write a particular report for a specialised proposal his company was putting together and knew she had the specific skills he needed. The job would probably only take three days at most, but Anna didn't like him or the company. In fact, her experience of them was that they treated people badly and paid low wages to their staff. She didn't want the job.

Up until this point, Anna had been loath to charge a lot for her services as a consultant because she felt she wasn't terribly experienced and didn't have much confidence in herself. However, in this case she decided she didn't want the job so much that she would ask a ridiculous sum of money to put her ex-employer off. That way, she wouldn't have to make some other excuse. She set her price, weighing up the following: given her current workload and her feelings about this job, what amount of money would make it worth her while? In other words, if they paid her x amount, she would do it. Well, you can guess what happened next. Her 'silly' fee was accepted and she was absolutely happy to do the work given how much she was getting!

The valuable lesson in the case study above is that we are only worth what we think we are worth. If you think you are not experienced enough, not old enough, not good enough and so on, you are. Sometimes we set limits for ourselves that only exist in our imagination. If you are good at what you do, once you are established you will be able to raise your fees and your clients will stay with you. If clients are getting what they want, they are happy with you and your reputation is growing, they will pay more.

Maximising your income

Aside from taking on other people (growing your business) or supplementing your earnings with other income streams aligned with your business, there are really only three ways to increase your income:

1. Obtain more clients

This really is a numbers game. The people who are successful at selling more (of anything) are simply those who make more calls – they just ask more people. Out of every 10 people you talk to about personal training, only a small number will be ready to buy your particular product at that particular moment. Let's say, for example, that one person out of every 10 will hire you as a personal trainer; it therefore makes complete sense that if you ask 100 people, you will get 10 new clients. This is why marketing and networking are so important. You will know from working with your clients that in order to see results you need to set goals. So, set yourself a goal to speak to at least 10 new people every week about personal training. Use all the tips in the networking and marketing sections (pages 37–40 and 33–7 respectively) to give you ideas about how to do this. Remember, though, that you can only train clients for a finite number of hours each week in order to avoid burnout. Once your practice is full do not keep on gaining new clients, unless you want to take on trainers underneath you and increase your business that way.

2. Charge more money

There are several ways to charge more per session. First, there is the issue of personal confidence and value described above, but there may be other areas where you are unwittingly doing yourself out of several thousands of pounds per year. For example, the 'free trial' session is not always valued and, if you are doing your marketing right and attracting lots of new clients, you may be giving away several free hours every week. Here are three ways to increase your profits in the free trial session:

- charge a fee, but make it less than your normal one so that clients still feel they are getting a 'good deal';
- charge a lower fee and offer the trial session or 'introduction' in small groups;
- offer a money-back guarantee – this is a really powerful marketing tool as potential clients are impressed by someone who is so confident in their skills that they offer a guarantee; also, people very rarely ask for their money back.

3. Work longer hours

You can do this by increasing the number of sessions each client buys. Do not presume that a client will only come and see you once a week. There will be some clients for whom it is appropriate to see you only once a month, but there will be others who would welcome the prospect of seeing you two or even three times per week.

There is huge debate over whether it is best to charge one fee to everyone and not discount to anyone at any time. This gives a perception of value and also means that you are never turning down fully paid sessions because you have previously booked in discounted ones. Remember too that some wealthy people will choose the most expensive item or service, not because it is better, but because they perceive that it is.

If you do decide to offer a sliding scale, here are some tips:

- Offer different price schemes for different levels of service. For example, if you travel to clients' homes, you may choose to charge more, taking into consideration travel time, convenience for your client and the equipment you need to bring with you. Perhaps you could offer on-line coaching between sessions or nutritional analysis for an extra fee. Whatever it is you offer, make sure there is enough of a difference in the service to justify the extra expense on your clients' part.
- Offer a discount if people block-book sessions with you.
- Offer a discount for off-peak sessions. In all probability, most of your sessions will take place early in the morning or after 5pm Monday to Friday. You may want to increase the number of hours you work in the middle of the day, so it can be useful to offer the less desirable slots at a slightly lower price.

Asking your clients for payment

Some people have real difficulty in asking for money. To make it easier, it is important to lay out all aspects of your pricing policy in your terms and conditions. Talk these through with your potential client, ensuring they understand your policies and fees.

It is not advisable to have your clients pay you per session as it takes time out of every session, can be awkward, is less professional and may lead to problems or embarrassment if, for whatever reason, your client cannot pay you on the day or if they cancel at short notice. Invoicing a month in advance is the best method. In this way you will be in control should your client cancel at the last minute or be late. You will also be more in control of your finances, making it easier and less time-consuming to organise that side of your business.

Self-employment – managing your finances

As a self-employed personal trainer, you will need to register with the tax office and arrange to pay your own national insurance contributions and will need to fill in a tax return every year. You can either do this yourself or get an accountant to do it for you. Either way, you will need to keep full and accurate records of all your business finances. Professional advice is crucial in this area, but as a start here are a few tips:

- Inform the Inland Revenue within three months of starting up your business or you may be fined. They will give you a Unique Tax Reference Number and will register you for Class II National Insurance contributions.
- Choose the 6th April as the start of your financial year. Your year will thus run from 6th April until 5th April the following year. This will make your job easier when it comes to working out your accounts because this is the standard tax year as set by the Inland Revenue.
- Open a separate bank account to deal with your personal training business. Your personal training income must not be mixed up with your everyday finances. If this is not possible, ensure you clearly show your business transactions as separate from your personal ones.
- You need to keep track of your income and also your expenses. You will want your expenses to be as high as possible as they will offset your tax liabilities. For this reason, it is important to clarify with your accountant exactly what you can and can't claim for when it comes to expenses. Keep every single receipt, no matter how small, and every bill pertaining to your business. If you run your office from home, don't forget to include a portion of your home-running costs as well. If you have receipts for equipment that you purchased before you started your business, but that you will be using in your business, you can get capital allowances on these too. Ask your accountant about the seven-year 'pre-trading expenses' that you can put through as a sole trader.
- Buy some folders. Display books are really useful for this purpose. One should be entitled 'expenses'. Label each page by month – the first will be 'April', then 'May' and so on. Then, every time you have a business expense – be it petrol, a training course, a phone bill or whatever – just drop the receipt into the appropriate month. This makes it so much easier to put all the information onto a spreadsheet and fill in your tax return than if you just shove all your receipts into a plastic bag. In addition, it is a far better way of keeping your receipts should you ever need them. Another file could be for your invoices. You could display your invoices monthly in the same way as your receipts, but the most important thing is to produce invoices for every piece of work you do and then keep any invoices to pay separate from invoices paid. This will enable you to see at a glance who you need to chase up for payment.
- Invoicing your clients on a monthly basis is the easiest way to keep track of payments. Use an appointment book to track sessions, making sure you make a note if a client cancels (and when they cancelled) or is late.
- The easiest way to keep track of your

finances is on a computer. There are loads of really good financial packages available that make the process much easier (see page 144 for some suggestions).

- Put money aside for your tax bill. It can be daunting to suddenly discover you have to find a large sum of money all in one go – far easier to put aside money each month. Your tax is due for payment at the end of January each year for the previous tax year and at the end of July on account for the current year. In essence, you will have to pay a tax bill twice a year at those times. If you can, put away 12–15 per cent of your earnings into a high-interest savings account. That way, you will have enough money to pay your tax and National Insurance bills and you will have earned interest as well!
- If you are using an accountant, keep their fee down by giving them as much detailed information as you can. For example, sort your expenses into categories such as petrol or travel, clothing, training, insurance products, professional memberships, equipment and so on, then tally up each different category so that you have a total amount for the year. In addition, get your information to the accountant early. The more they have to keep badgering you to get the information to them, the more your costs go up.

Putting a small amount of effort into organising yourself in advance will save you hours of work later on and will save you quibbling with clients over misunderstandings.

Getting organised

Michael Gerber, author of *The E-Myth Revisited*, developed the concept of working *on* your business, not just *in* your business. Have you ever worked so hard at personal training, or indeed any job or business, that you never had time to actually build the business, plan for the future, develop new projects or even decide if this is really how you want to earn a living? Well, life can be very busy and the only way to actually consider these ideas is to make time for them. In the same way that you would advise a client to make exercise or fitness appointments with themselves in their diary, you need to put planning time into your diary when you can work on your business. This means time out from the everyday stuff of training clients, going on training courses yourself, networking and everything else you do.

At the beginning of each year, buy yourself a planner or use your computer planner and mark out your holidays and planning time – this can be as short or as long as you want. The system has to work for you, so there is no right or wrong way of doing this. Just mark out the time and guard it well – this time is precious. It is the time to dream, to build and to plan for your future. It could be one hour every Monday morning, when you focus on your goals and plan what you are going to do that week to take you closer to it; it could be a day a month or even a week every six months when you go away on your own and just plan. Again, what you do with this time is entirely personal, but it may include any or all of the following:

- 'mind mapping' your dreams and projects. Mind mapping is a technique developed by Tony Buzan in the 1960s, and is now used by adults, children and major companies. It works on the basis that our minds don't think in a linear fashion, so when you need to be creative or work on an idea or project, mind mapping is a way of eliciting information from yourself. You start by writing the topic in the centre of a piece of paper and, from there, drawing lines to take you to the next idea and the next (see Figure 3.1). In this way, your mind can work by linking ideas to

Figure 3.1 Mind mapping your personal training business

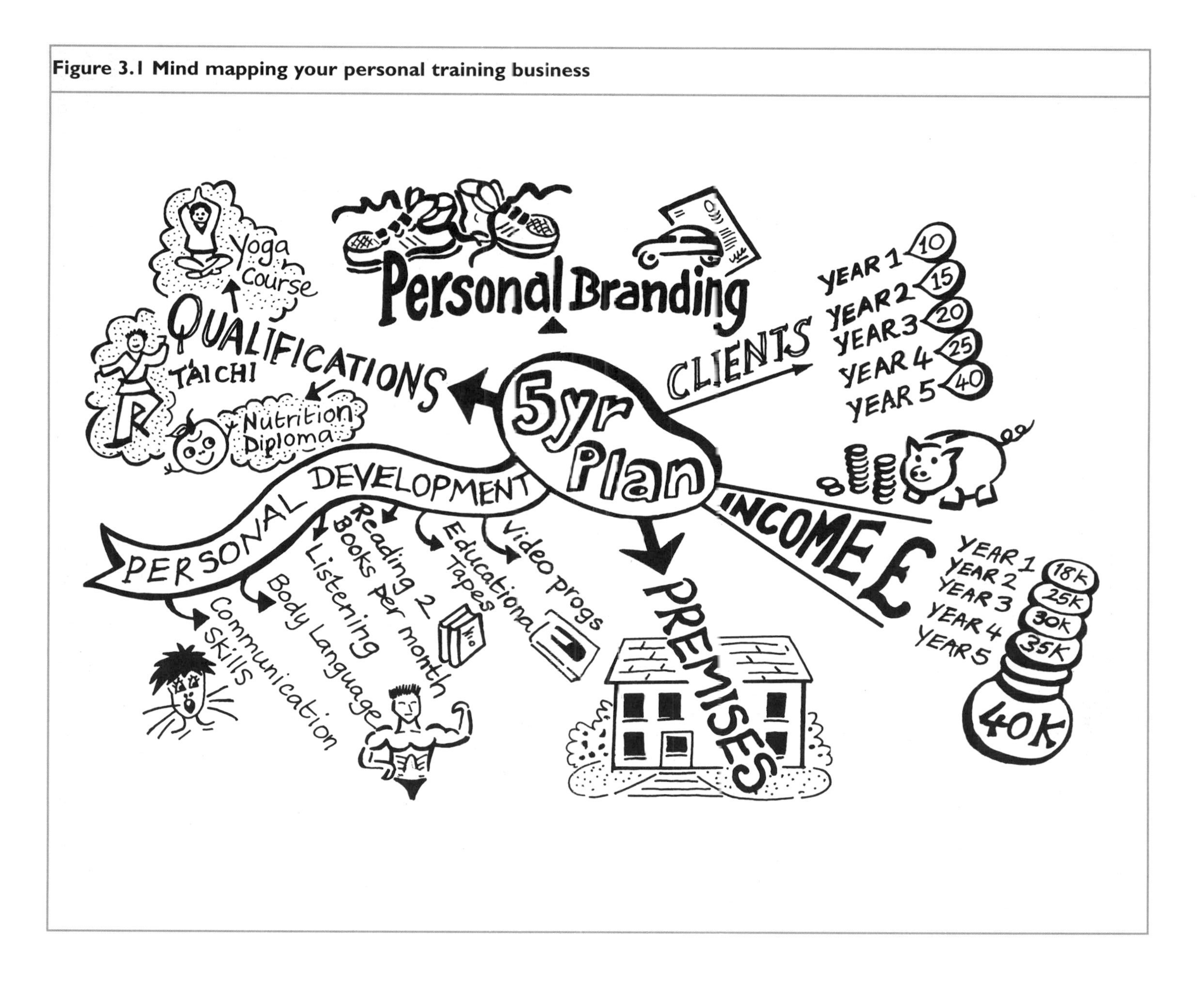

ideas. Working with colour and drawing pictures into your mind maps also help you to think creatively. Mind maps help you to collect random ideas and slot them together, creating a plan that is graphically clear so that you can collect thoughts around a whole project on one page and link seemingly separate ideas together;
- going on a business seminar or workshop (not necessarily on the technical business of personal training);
- meeting up with a mentor or business partner to come up with ideas to drive your business forward. Ideas come much more quickly when you can discuss them out loud;
- planning your marketing strategy for the next six months. Most personal trainers don't think any further than their next appointment, let alone the next six months, so actually planning a marketing strategy over a period of time will put you leagues ahead of the rest of the personal training pack.

Seeing your year laid out and taking a strategic view of your business will drive you forward and stop you getting caught up in the day-to-day business of it all, feeling like you are getting nowhere.

Systems for success

Any business can only be as good as the systems that help it to run. It is far too easy to get qualified and then to start on day one by sitting around waiting for your personal mobile phone to ring. It is important to look at every aspect of your personal training business as just that – a business – and to develop systems around each area. So, going back to the mobile phone as an example, you need to ask yourself the right questions that will then prompt you to set up a system. So, what kind of phone line will you use for your business? It is good to have a mobile number, but also a landline as people trust businesses with landlines. In each case, do not use your personal line for business purposes. You can get two telephone numbers attached to one mobile phone these days, which can be really useful. You can then leave a professional outgoing message for your business line and a more casual one for your personal use. The same goes for the home message. Think about what should be on your outgoing message. Will it be updated daily so that people know when they can contact you directly? If people do leave a message, how long will it take for you to return it? If you have a policy of returning all calls within 24 hours, how will you ensure your promise is always kept?

You get the point. Think about all the aspects of your business that require some thought around systems and list what those systems might be. These may include:

- Marketing – promotion, networking, materials such as business cards
- Financial – invoicing, pricing, budgeting, chasing late payments
- Telephone – see above
- Appointments – making, cancelling, re-scheduling
- Website – branding, updates
- Client contacts – prospective enquiries, records and notes, complaints

Setting up your 'office'

Make sure you have a dedicated space from which to run your business. It is really important to think of your office as a business and to set up everything you would expect from any business you might deal with. If you do not have an office away from home, be sure that you set some space aside within your own home where you can get organised. This does not have to be an entire room – it could just be a corner of your living room – but it does need to be separate in some way. It will help you to focus if you always go to a specific area to get your work done. In the same way, you need to be able to shut off at the end of the day; if your work is all over the place you will never really get away from it, which can be very exhausting. In addition, having all of your files in one place leads to greater organisation and saves time as you don't have to look for things elsewhere.

You also need to think about the function of your office and how much time you will spend there. Will you be seeing clients in your office, or is it only for you to organise your work? In either case, make sure it is a welcoming and comfortable environment. Make sure it is well lit and quiet with enough work and storage space and a comfortable chair or chairs. Keep everything you will need for office work close at hand. That means making sure you have paper clips, pens, pencils, paper, stapler, stamps, your calendar or appointment book, business cards, phone book, scissors and envelopes within easy reach.

The telephone

It is a good idea to have a dedicated phone line from which to run your business. That way you can turn your phone off when you are not working – there will always be clients who think it's OK to call you at midnight! Make sure you have a message facility and that the outgoing message you leave for callers is clear, professional and up to date. For example, state your name (or business name) and date (if you change your message daily to state when people can speak to you in person). Keep your message brief and keep to the point – have you ever dreaded calling a particular business because every time you do you have to sit and wait through a long-winded message? Make sure your voice is upbeat and friendly – you want to leave your clients with the impression that you are pleased they called. Also, periodically call your own phone to make sure the message is audible. Some answering machines can make recordings sound very messy and difficult to hear, which makes you look unprofessional and could irritate people. Make sure you check your messages regularly and always get back to people promptly. This may all sound like obvious advice, but it is amazing how many people give an unfavourable impression of themselves from this issue alone. Think for yourself how you like to be treated when you ring a business and you will realise just how frustrating bad telephone service can be.

Paperwork

It doesn't really matter how you organise your work so long as you do organise it! Some people like to use their computer to file everything, but most of us still find that we generate endless amounts of paper. The following is a list of files you may need:

- client documentation – filed alphabetically and including contact details, agreements, emergency contact details, PAR-Q (now adopted as an industry standard, the original 'PAR-Q and You' is owned and copyrighted by the Canadian Society for Exercise Physiology), programme notes and history, fitness assessment results and so on;
- paperwork pertaining to your business such as insurance, equipment warranties, professional memberships;
- a documented portfolio of your qualifications, certificates, personal developments, achievements, testimonials and published articles. This is not only useful in that you will be able

to lay your hands on this information easily, but it is also good to be able to show this kind of thing to prospective clients;

- financial paperwork. If this is the first time you have run a business, make sure you get some professional advice about what paperwork you need to keep and for how long. For example, you should keep tax returns for five years and, if you are self-employed, you should keep everything to do with your business for six years. In order to keep your own accounts, you will need to keep your finances perfectly organised so that you can pull your annual accounts together quickly when you need to complete your tax return;
- client packs. These will probably be held electronically, but there will be a lot of paperwork that needs to be given to your clients and you will have to organise it well on your computer so that you can access what you need quickly. Folders might include a start-up pack with a welcome letter, forms, your terms and conditions, articles, your biography, ongoing offers that you can pull out for clients at certain times (offering added value to your service), marketing packs and different set programmes so that you are not constantly reinventing the wheel.

It really is worth taking the time to organise yourself to avoid wasting time wading through endless piles of paperwork before you find what you need.

Tools, gadgets, lists and tricks

Make sure you have a good time management system. Again, it really doesn't matter what it is so long as it works for you. Some of the most successful businessmen and women still prefer to use a simple small appointment calendar and pencil. (Using a pencil in your diary is always a good idea because it is easy to change appointments; crossed-out appointments start to look really messy and make it harder to see sessions at a glance.)

'To do' lists are vital to running an effective business. Again, everyone is different – you may prefer to use a PDA or be happy with pen and paper. Keeping that list updated is crucial to feeling in control. At the end of each day, plan what you need to do the next day so you can go to bed knowing that you are prepared and hit the ground running in the morning. If you are one of those people who always seem to have an endless 'to do' list, try one or two of these tricks to stop feeling overwhelmed and never accomplishing everything: prioritise your list so that you get the most important things done early on; schedule time into your day to do the things you have been putting off; and if your list seems out of control, pick just three things you will get done that day. This helps you to focus on the things that will make a difference and will also make you feel like you are getting somewhere.

Setting up your own gym

Having been in the industry for several years, you may decide you would like to spread your wings and create a larger business of your own. It is a very appealing thought to be able to design and build your own gym and choose your staff, systems and levels of customer care. In addition, your business income will no longer be entirely dependent on you training clients yourself. In the long term, this means you can earn even when you are not working.

If you do your research, pick the right location and create a sound business plan, the sky is the limit and the rewards of setting up your own gym can be huge. On the other hand, the risks are also enormous. A huge number of new businesses fail within the first few months, so you must be prepared to work very hard at first and take the time to build things up slowly; your income in the short term might even be lower than if you were working as a freelance personal trainer.

This section only offers a broad overview. If you have the entrepreneurial spirit and aspire to setting up your own studio or gym, it is essential that you do your research and get sound business start-up advice as employing staff brings with it many legal duties and responsibilities. In addition, setting up your own gym is not a decision to be taken lightly as you are likely to need substantial backing to get a project like this off the ground.

Starting your own studio requires 100 per cent of your effort and you will need focus, determination, organisation and a large amount of resources with everything documented. You will need to know the fitness business well, be confident in your abilities as a personal trainer and have a solid client base to bring to the new company. You will need your own place of operation that you either own or lease and staff with set roles and responsibilities, as well as a healthy operating bank account to begin with. You are entering into a contractually binding agreement with your landlord for a number of years, so you need to be sure that you are ready for the legal and financial obligations that go along with this.

Having said that, running your own studio and employing a bunch of 'mini-mes' is hugely rewarding: not only are you helping to improve the health and well-being of your members, but you are also helping to grow and develop your staff.

Benefits and drawbacks of setting up your own studio

Complete control

By having your very own place of operation you are 100 per cent responsible for the internal and external branding of the studio. This is why you will need to have worked for several years gaining this experience on a small scale as a working personal trainer. No-one else can dictate to you what you can and can't do, what you can and can't wear and how to operate. However, this also means that a thorough understanding of what works is vital to the success of your new venture. It is your operation and you will live or die by your own decisions, style and operating procedures. You will therefore need to be resourceful and possibly have access to others who can help you in areas you are not so confident in. Do not underestimate the amount of work needed to set everything up and source suppliers. Complete control can also be an isolating experience as the buck stops with you. Staff will be depending on you to show leadership and make important decisions.

Company structure

You will be director of your own company and be able to benefit from the large number of tax advantages that this structure will provide. A good accountant or tax specialist will be able to let you know what these are and help you to maximise the benefits.

Money

By running your own business you will be more able to truly leverage your time and achieve passive income. You need to focus on running the business rather than the business running you. However, bear in mind that if it is the personal training side of your job that you love, you will have less time to do it if you are running your own gym as you will need to focus on the business side of things as well. In fact, the main complaint of many ambitious personal trainers who either go into leisure management or end up running their own business is that they sometimes find they miss the actual personal training element – the very thing they were passionate about (people and training) is the thing they miss the most. Losing touch with clients and the training side can be too big a jump for some people, so do consider this in your plans.

You also need to consider the amount of risk involved in setting up your venture and again take advice from an accountant to minimise your liabilities.

Recognition

By having your own studio you immediately move up to the next level of the industry and begin to acquire a sense of status within the community; this will open more doors and create more opportunities for you. Be prepared to rise to these expectations and don't miss any opportunities that may be offered to you. You must also be careful to balance these opportunities with your core business and avoid being overstretched. Remember, the higher you go, the further you can fall, so build things slowly and securely to ensure success.

Management

Having your own studio will mean managing people. You will spend more time developing your staff and educating them on your theories of movement and exercise than actually dealing with members. You will lead, direct and focus the efforts of your staff so they can deliver your ideas. This can be immensely rewarding, but developing management skills will be another hurdle to get over if you do not already have any experience in this area.

Professional services you may find useful

The list below is by no means exhaustive, but in setting up your studio you may need help from the following people to do things properly:

- **Accountant** – an accountant will almost certainly be necessary to help you with the technical issues involved in growing your business and possibly taking on staff. An accountant will prepare your tax return for the Inland Revenue and deal with them on your behalf.
- **Lawyer** – there are many legal issues involved with setting up your own business and contracts will need to be drawn up for staff, premises and so on.
- **Book-keeper** – unless you have skills in this area, a book-keeper is essential to keep your business on track financially and to keep records of all financial transactions for your accountant.
- **Bank manager** – you may need a bank loan and will almost certainly need to create a business plan for your bank manager.
- **Graphic designer** – it is worth your while employing the services of a graphic designer to help you create a great image and branding and to streamline this across the business (see also pages 40–44).

Minimum staff requirements

Choosing and interviewing staff is an art in itself. Ideally, you will have some experience in this area as employing the wrong staff can be costly both in time and money. You should compile job descriptions (exactly what your staff will be required to do) and person specifications (what qualifications and experience they must have) prior to taking anyone on board. You will also need to consider your interview process. How many of you will interview? It can be good to get a trusted colleague or business partner to help in this process. What questions will you ask? Will candidates be required to 'audition'? Where will you advertise?

Hopefully you will see there is a lot to consider in the process of taking on staff. You will, of course, require that any personal trainer you take on is qualified (and remember you can choose what 'qualified' means, but you would be advised to use REPs for guidance). You may also require they have up-to-date CPR or first aid and that they are members of REPs. Below is a list of other, perhaps less obvious, skills that you may want to look for in your staff.

Looking the part

It's a team thing and you and your team will be judged by the way you look. Ensuring that your staff are clean and tidy with shirts tucked in and neat hair will help this. Having a designated smart and stylish uniform will lift your studio's image and help your staff feel good about who they work for.

Attitude

You are in the people business, so obviously your staff must be friendly, bubbly and have a strong customer focus. They must have a winning attitude, so having a carefully scripted interview process whereby you ensure that you address the question of attitude will enable you to pick up on your potential employees' attitude.

Professionalism

Your whole operation must smell of complete professionalism. This will start with you, and will have a filter-down effect to your staff: your staff will look to you for their standards, thus you must always be completely on your game. You must think about the image you wish to portray, not only to your members but also to your staff.

Confidence

Your clients will expect your staff to take charge – they are the fitness professionals, after all. They must be able to take charge of your members; this means not only must your members have confidence in them, but so too must you. You must feel comfortable leaving your members in your employees' hands.

Reliability

Your staff must be reliable when delivering your product: they must be on time, stay in touch with your members and do whatever it takes to get the results your members want.

Minimum professional requirements

When moving to the level of owning your own studio, having solid documentation is vital. By the nature and size of the operation you are entering into, you simply will not have the time to do every task required. Thus you will need to enlist the help of your staff to share the load. For your staff to be effective, everything needs to be in written form so that they have something to follow and come back to. Systems will help you manage your time and make you more efficient. When you have designed your systems, create an 'operations manual'. You will find this an invaluable tool because all of your systems, forms, documentation and procedures will be found in one place. In this way, you can ensure that the documentation you are using is the most up-to-date version (you simply replace old versions as they get updated) and new staff can learn what systems they should use quickly and efficiently. The operations manual should only contain information that is useful to everyone in your company, such as common procedures and information. It is not the appropriate place for confidential information or procedures that only you will carry out as the business owner.

Business plan

Along with your operations manual, your business plan is probably the most important document your business needs. Without a solid business plan your chances of success are hugely diminished. Your business plan should outline all the things you plan to do in your first year and everything your business will attempt to do, and should also attach projected monetary values to your operation. It should be specific and detailed and clearly outline the steps you will take in order to make your business work.

External branding

This means thinking about what it will be like for your members to be part of your studio – the look, feel and image of your operation.

Internal branding

As a self-employed personal trainer you have to think about external branding, but when you own your own studio you also have to think about internal branding. This means what it is like to work for your company, what the culture is like, how things get done and the general vibe of your workplace.

Premises contract

This should be a solid document that outlines the parameters of your relationship with your landlord and how you can use the premises.

Staff contracts

Whether your staff are employees or contractors, the contracts need to set out the nature of the relationship, pay structures, termination clauses and terms and conditions.

Operations manual

This sets out how your business is run, how your customers pay, member flow, exercise prescription, what services you provide for members, package options and what items and services you sell. It should include banking processes, opening and closing procedures, staff pay systems and anything to do with the smooth running of the studio.

Member forms

These should include the following:

- pre-activity questionnaire
- needs analysis
- body-fat assessments
- postural and movement screening
- exercise prescription cards
- cardio programmes
- stretch programmes
- class options.

Having a starter pack for each member will also increase your studio's perceived value. Again, this will be similar to what you did as a sole trader, but you will want to standardise procedures for your studio business to ensure quality control.

Internal communication system

This should cover anything that needs to be communicated between staff members regarding clients' training, operational difficulties, equipment failure and anything else that needs to be circulated among the staff.

External communication system

This covers the information members receive once they have joined your studio, such as newsletters, memos, emails and any communication between the studio and the member.

Marketing plan

Draw up a 12-month marketing plan, making sure it is detailed, specific and on a month-by-month basis. See Chapter 4 for more on marketing.

Sales system

Have sales scripts and systems for your sales team to follow, minimum performance criteria for your sales reps and a database linking your sales leads, appointments, conversions and referrals.

Studio layout and design

What equipment and gear do you have, where is it located and what is its usage? Do the layout and equipment match your ideas on exercise prescription? Does the layout allow for group training, and if so how many people can train together at a time?

Getting started

So how do you get started? The information above gives you a brief taste of some of the issues involved in running your own studio or gym. If you are an experienced personal trainer and still want to go ahead and set up your own business, you need a place to start. You will need to research and plan what you intend to do before seeking funding (if necessary) and eventually promoting and launching your venture.

Planning

Location

What is your target market and where will your studio be based? Do your homework on the area you wish to service: what are the demographics of the people that live or work in the area? What is their disposable income? Who are they and what do they do for work? How much will rent be in the area? What options are available for facilities?

Client base

By the time you are ready to move to your own studio you will already be servicing a number of clients. This asset base will move with you to your new premises, thus giving you instant cash flow once operations start.

Promotion

Foundation memberships

A foundation membership is one that you sell while you are renovating or constructing the premises. You can pre-sell memberships, which could include special offers or discounts for purchasing before the facility is open. This is another excellent way of ensuring good cash flow upon opening.

Marketing and promotion

This is a matter of following your business and marketing plans to the letter. By having your sales department follow the system you have created, you should quickly establish a strong membership base.

Launch

Have a launch party and invite key business personnel from your area. Allied health professionals are an excellent start. Try to attract a local celebrity if you know one and try to get some media exposure in the social pages of your local newspaper or on your local radio station. You can organise it yourself or hire a PR consultant to do the work for you – at this point you probably have many things on your plate, so the secret is to maximise your time and direct it to the most important tasks.

Massive action

Be prepared to take huge amounts of action and do huge amounts of work to get your project off the ground. Your first three months will be crucial to your studio's success. It is time to roll up your sleeves and get on with it.

Top tips for filling your personal training practice

To end this chapter, here are some tips on how to fill your business, whether you are a sole trader or are running your own studio:

1. Give something for nothing.
2. Ask existing clients for referrals.
3. Reward clients when they send you referrals by sending a card, flowers or taking them out for lunch. At the very least, acknowledge referrals quickly by telephone or text.
4. Under-promise and over-deliver.
5. Always be positive and constructive.
6. Take time to focus before every session so that your clients get your full attention and energy.
7. Set high standards for yourself – and keep them!
8. Send out a monthly newsletter.
9. Always dress well and behave professionally.
10. Do hand out a business card, but always ask permission to call.
11. Be interested in your clients and prospective clients.
12. Listen more than you speak.
13. Always do what you say you are going to do.
14. Never gossip.
15. Take enough holidays.
16. Tailor your personal training business to what people want to buy, not to what you want to sell.
17. Lead a workshop for your clients at no extra charge.
18. Lead a workshop for the public or speak to different groups (public speaking).
19. Join clubs/organisations where you might meet prospective clients.
20. Send postcards to your clients while you (or they!) are away. Send birthday cards as well.
21. Invest in your own ongoing training and development.
22. Ensure you lead a balanced life and get what you need outside of your business.
23. Ensure that any branded resources, such as business cards, flyers, adverts and T-shirts, are spectacular.
24. Finish every session on a high, be it a warm smile, a sincere thank you or a positive message.
25. Know your limitations and refer clients on as necessary.
26. Be demanding in your expectations of yourself and your clients.
27. Learn to describe your business in a short snappy sentence.

MARKETING

4

In this chapter you will:

- understand the five Ps of marketing and how they apply to your business
- learn how to network
- learn how to build a brilliant brand
- explore cost-effective marketing strategies for your business.

In Chapter 3 we talked about finding out who your clients are and specialising. This has huge relevance when it comes to marketing – by identifying a target market, you will get some ideas as to where to start your marketing campaign. Becoming an expert in a field differentiates you from the rest and can help lead clients to your door – if you get the marketing right! Having a specialism allows you to charge far more than your competitors. If you think about any other industry, specialists charge far more than all-rounders. In the healthcare field, Harley Street specialists (seen as the 'experts') are able to charge a premium for their services.

The five Ps of marketing

Marketing is the process by which you get your prospective clients' attention, get them to hire you and then keep them as clients. To this end, you will need to look at how you define yourself and your product, how you promote yourself as a personal trainer and the relationship you build with your clients.

Marketing theory consists of the five Ps: product, positioning, place, price and promotion. Each 'P' connects with the others to create an accurate marketing tool. You cannot leave any out or your whole proposition will be diluted. Worse, if you get even one element wrong, your whole marketing message could be ruined. For example, if you promote your product well, have superb positioning, choose a great location but get your pricing all wrong, you will fall at the first hurdle. Every element of this is intrinsically linked and serves to influence the others. You need to get the whole package right in order to do a good marketing job.

Product

In this case the product is personal training. There are some things you should evaluate. What are the benefits of hiring a personal trainer? You may have heard the term 'WIIFM' or 'What's In It For Me?'. Think about your service from a prospective client's point of view. What's in it for them? In other words, they are not buying personal training as such, but instead a better body, more energy, better posture or whatever other benefit they might want. You need to make your prospective clients realise that they need a personal trainer in order to do this before moving on to the next 'P', which will tell them they need you specifically.

Positioning

This refers to your position within the personal training market – what makes you unique? You may have heard of the term USP, or unique selling point. Your USP is the benefit you would offer to your target market. The idea of positioning is to help you get the market's attention over and above your competitors – that is, once you are clear about why people need a personal trainer, you now need to think about why they need you specifically.

The following is a great equation to illustrate the idea of positioning:

$$USP = MD + FD$$

MD stands for 'major differentiator'. This is the one thing that sets you apart from everyone else. It must be something that no-one else could have. For example, saying that you are great with beginners is not a major differentiator – the next personal trainer could also be great with beginners. If, however, you were to say 'nobody understands people in cardiac rehab. like me', that *would* be a major differentiator; you are saying that with your knowledge added to your personal qualities added to your vast experience, there is no-one like you.

FD stands for 'focused differentiators'. These are qualities that may not be major, but they are immensely important, such as 'I will never be late', 'I always give 100 per cent, I will not count reps and you will never find my attention wandering' or 'I am fantastic with kids'. Together with your major differentiator, this will give you your USP. You need to give this a lot of thought as it can communicate very powerfully.

Your USP may lead you to market segmentation, which can be split into three categories:

Mass or undifferentiated marketing

This means offering the same service to everyone and focusing on common needs. Many personal trainers use this method.

Product-variety or differentiated marketing

In this case, you would choose the market segments you want to work with, say older adults and pre- and post-natal exercise. You would then devise different offers for each market segment.

Target marketing or concentrated marketing

In this instance, you would simply aim for one market segment and become highly specialised.

You must ensure that, whatever your positioning, you offer a valued benefit to your target clients and that you are different enough from the competition to be distinctive in some way. You will need to be able to communicate this to prospective clients.

Place

In terms of a tangible product, 'place' would refer to how the product would be made available to the consumer. In the case of personal training, 'place' might apply to where you would train clients. Will you visit them at home or do you operate out of a gym or studio? Perhaps you will visit your clients in their work place? Whatever you decide, make sure you are clear what the options are.

'Place' may also refer to how you would communicate with prospective clients.

Price

This is self-explanatory. However, the price you choose to charge for your services is a decision that should not be made lightly. You can see why positioning should come before price – you must be clear about your USP and your target market before you can even think about the price you will charge. Clearly, if you set your price too high, you may not appeal to as many clients as you might wish to; set it too low, however, and you run the risk of not being seen as a personal trainer of any quality. Indeed, there is a segment of the population who will only buy in the higher price range simply because it is more expensive, the logic being that if it is expensive, it must be good!

The price you charge communicates a lot about your service. If you think about it, a reasonable or 'cheap' price may say that you offer value for money or that you are accessible to everyone. However, it may also say you are not very good, not in demand or newly qualified with little experience. These are obviously not the things you plan to communicate, but people will interpret your service based partly on price. Think about it in terms of supermarkets if you want a simple example. If you were to visit a deprived area, what sort of supermarket names would you expect to see there? What products would they sell? What would they not sell? What type of people shop there? Then think about an affluent area. Again, what sort of supermarkets would you find there? What products? What sort of people? There is no right way of doing this. You just need your price to fit with the rest of your package and think about the message you want to send out.

There are a couple of other issues to take into account in setting up your pricing strategy:

- You may choose to offer a set price for your services, but you could offer a range of different levels of service at different prices, as discussed on page 20. For example, you could offer silver, gold and platinum services: the silver service could include training only; gold could include on-line support in between sessions; and platinum could include a little extra service on top of the other two, such as regular dietary analysis, phone support or more comprehensive fitness testing. If this is the case, you will need to set up clear price steps between the different levels.
- You could choose to sell other items on top of your personal training business, such as nutritional supplements, books or equipment. If you go down this route, make sure that you do so ethically and only with the good of your client in mind. Never try to sell items purely to make a profit, regardless of client benefit. You will very quickly lose credibility and your entire practice could be in jeopardy.

See pages 18–19 for more information on pricing your services.

Promotion

The objective of promotion is to move the customer along the following cycle: unawareness; awareness; beliefs/knowledge; attitude; purchase intention; and, finally, purchase. This model is very similar to a couple of elements in the Stages of Change (see pages 125–6); although the latter relates to behaviour modification, it is a similar process. First, you want to move the customer from unawareness to awareness. This is very similar to moving them from pre-contemplation to contemplation – basically, they need to become aware of you. During the awareness phase (similar to contemplation), the prospective customer is considering whether to take action – in this case to hire you. In order to help them in the process and move them along to purchase intention, you may need to challenge existing beliefs, update their knowledge of what personal training is or of what exercise could do for them and help them to alter their attitude to personal training and, specifically, to you. Once they have the purchase intention (or preparation in the Cycle of Change), you then need to move them to take action – in this case to hire you as their personal trainer. This is the sole aim of promotion. It applies not only to advertising but also to any way in which you promote your personal training business, such as chatting to members in a gym (only do this where you already work as a personal trainer and where you have an agreement with the management that you can do this), writing a regular column for a local newspaper or speaking at public events.

In designing your promotion, you must identify what the offer is – what do you want the prospective client to do? Always direct people to what you want them to do next. At the end of a talk, for example, it might be for them to leave their name, telephone number and e-mail address. (N.B. a good contact list is everything. Give away something to encourage people to leave you their details: a fact sheet is a good example of something that costs very little to produce but offers value to prospective customers, thus persuading them to leave their details with you.) If you place an advert in the local newspaper, the direction might be to 'call this number to book your introductory session'. If you offer a promotion to get referrals from current clients, tell your clients what to do. For example, you could design a card or leaflet that tells them what they will get, exactly how to put their friend or relative in touch with you and at what point they can earn their reward (say, after the client has completed or paid for four sessions). This is a very good way of growing your business, as most new clients will come from your current customer base, and people are more likely to refer if a reward is involved.

However you decide to promote your services, try to track where your clients come from so that you can gauge which methods work best. You could do this by putting a reference code in the advert for people to quote when they call you or asking where people heard of you on your introductory questionnaire. There is no point in forking out loads of money on expensive advertising campaigns if the majority of your clients come from word of mouth.

Some of the ways you might choose to promote your services are listed below.

World Wide Web

Having your own website gives you credibility and provides a way for prospective clients to check you out before they call you. It is a relatively cheap way of reaching people and the web is the first place many people look for anything nowadays. However, it can be hard to get yourself noticed on it. Employing a good technician in this area can pay a fortune in dividends and make the difference between your site being the world's best-kept secret or the first site people find in their search for a personal trainer.

Direct mail

With only about a 1 per cent response rate, this is probably not the best form of advertising for a service like personal training, unless you are perhaps opening a new studio and you mail-shot the immediate locality. It is quite a specialised and detailed project to undertake and will only get you limited results; there are many variables that could affect success, such as the mailing list, your target audience, the design of your mail, timing and the offer itself.

Advertisements

Newspaper or magazine adverts can be costly and, depending on which one you advertise in, may have limited use. Classified adverts are more affordable and allow you to run your ad on a more regular basis. Think very carefully about the publication and whether its readership is your target audience. If you can, get the publication to send you a media kit, which should tell you about prices, circulation information and reader profile. Clearly, you will want local clients, so it is always better to advertise in local publications.

Building a public profile

To start building a public profile for yourself, start to give talks and seminars in your area of specialism. Write for your local newspaper or industry magazines.

Networking and referrals

Networking is about creating new contacts and using those relationships to create business success. Based on the fact that referrals and recommendations are a successful and cost-effective way to increase your client base, networking enables you to meet other professionals (not necessarily in fitness) and thereby generate leads and new business for one another.

Working as a personal trainer can be a very isolating experience and so the need to be a powerful networker cannot be overemphasised. According to Rob Brown, the UK's leading expert on turning relationships into profits, there are many benefits to networking. Networking means you can:

- uncover new business opportunities
- make more profits and more money
- meet or exceed targets for bonuses and commissions, or simply safeguard your job in tough economic times
- recruit your next employee or business partner
- raise your personal profile
- source great suppliers
- locate new joint venture partners or strategic alliances
- improve your self-confidence and self-esteem
- make your mark in a new role or territory
- enjoy the challenge and thrill of winning new business
- learn new ideas, industry tips and insider trends and information
- scout the competition
- maintain and 'go deeper' with your existing contacts and clients
- develop 'referral networks' by educating your contacts in exactly what you're looking for
- set up your network in order to change jobs or go out on your own
- meet new friends or gain a support system
- develop leadership skills (Brown, 2005).

There are many great places to network. In short, it's anytime, anyplace, anywhere! Look out for these in particular:

- trains, planes and automobiles!
- sporting events
- social events, bars, clubs and pubs
- formal networking clubs (see page 145 for some contact details)
- cafes, shops and restaurants
- one-off annual conferences, trade shows and exhibitions
- queues of any kind.

Case Study

A hugely successful conference speaker started out her career as many speakers do, presenting for free at Women's Institutes, Rotary Club events and so on. One particular event was a mother and baby group. She didn't think that the session could possibly get her any future business, but it was useful practice ground for new material. This particular speaker has a bubbly personality. She is a 'larger than life' character who adores people and speaks to everyone. She struck up a conversation after the session with a nervous, shy woman who had been quite profoundly moved by the speaker's words.

It turned out she was the wife of the Chief Executive of a multi-national company that was holding its annual conference a couple of months later. In short, this inexperienced speaker was asked to keynote that conference – a plum role for a first-timer and one that catapulted her career in double-quick time! So, you never know who people know!

So, how can you become more confident and effective in your networking? Here are the five golden rules that make networking work (Brown, 2005):

1. **Be open.** You never know how someone could be useful to your business. Never dismiss anyone because of preconceived ideas.
2. **Be proactive.** You are in a people business and your career depends entirely on getting on with people and providing exceptional customer care. What better way to start and to practise than to talk to as many people as possible? Make the first move, approach strangers, start conversations and ask questions to open people up and get them talking about themselves.
3. **Be patient.** Networking is simply building relationships, and this takes time. Part of networking is selling yourself, and you will do this best by being interested, not interesting – that is, by listening, learning, helping and asking what people need and how you can help. You should also keep in touch with people – even if someone does not need your services now, they may do in the future and you will want to be the first person they think of when that time comes.
4. **Be prepared.** Business cards, a big smile, good listening skills, a willingness to help, an expectant attitude, a 'non-salesy' approach and a bank of interesting questions and conversation openers should all be part of your networking toolkit, as well as the ability to spot the right event or occasion and the right people. This will help you to make the most of what is premium, precious time!
5. **Be committed.** By building professional networks, you will also increase your potential client base. Don't forget that when you make referrals or recommendations to other professionals, they will reciprocate by referring people to you when their friends, family, neighbours, acquaintances or clients are looking for an excellent personal trainer.

The power of referrals

Have you ever had a flood in your kitchen and had to trawl through the phone book to call out someone you didn't know? Have you ever suffered major toothache but didn't know a good, reliable (and kind) dentist? What would you do if your computer, containing all of your client information (contact details, assessment results, programmes) crashed? Would you know who to call?

It will be a huge advantage to you and your business if you have a list of dependable and skilled individuals held in some kind of list or database. Don't wait for an emergency to find the person you need. Not only will this be invaluable to you, but your clients will benefit too. Your reputation as an expert and as a trainer will rise dramatically if you can be depended on to always refer people to someone good. It also helps you to be clear about the services you can and cannot offer your clients. For example, you may be training someone who also wants to try yoga or Pilates. If you are not competent to teach these disciplines, don't be afraid to refer the client on to someone who is. You will not lose your client, and even if you do, your professionalism is likely to be rewarded in the long term.

Building up your referrals network

First of all, make a list of all the contacts that would be useful, both to you and your clients. Create networking spheres of people you know, value and trust. Here are a few to get you started:

- Massage therapist or sports massage therapist
- Alexander technique practitioner
- Sports psychologist
- Podiatrist
- Physiotherapist
- Osteopath
- Fellow personal trainers with particular specialisms
- Acupuncturist
- Chiropractor
- Nutritionist
- Accountant
- Doctor/GP
- Solicitor
- Financial advisor.

Next, you need to start building up your network. Here are some ideas to help you.

Ask friends and acquaintances

Ask everyone in your circle if they know a good doctor (or whatever). Most of us have a much wider circle than we think and, if we were to really think broadly, the number of people we know would run into the hundreds – if not thousands. Think about all the different communities you connect with in your life. In each community there will be people who know just what or whom you are looking for. Your communities might include gyms, your neighbourhood, clubs, church, school, family, friends, workplace and so on.

Once you have located these people, get in contact with them. It is important to spend time nurturing and building relationships. Most people love to be respected and consulted for their professional competence. However, you will need to give them a good reason to meet you. The offer of a free session with you and a good explanation as to what you want from the relationship (i.e. mutual referrals) is very useful. When you meet, find out how they like to work and get to know them. Ask them what sort of people they would like you to refer to them.

Join networking organisations

These exist solely for the purpose of putting professionals in contact with one another for support and referrals. One of the biggest of these organisations is Business Network International (see page 145 for contact details) whose local groups meet for an early breakfast meeting on a monthly basis. They only allow one member for each trade. So, you will not be competing against other personal trainers. The idea is to introduce people to your service and to share ideas and clients.

Attend conferences and other professional events

Many people attend conferences without getting the best out of them. Conferences are vital for keeping you up to date and in touch, but it is important to see the breaks between sessions as being as useful as the sessions themselves. That's when you get to meet fellow professionals who can become a part of your network, as well as giving you the opportunity to build on existing relationships. Find events by subscribing to leisure industry journals, reading local newspapers or contacting your local chamber of commerce.

Top networking tips

The skill of building and nurturing relationships is just that – a skill. It is all very well knowing what should be done, or seeing the benefits of networking, but learning how to do it is something else altogether! Here are some tips:

1. When you are at an event and want to meet people, look for groups of more than two people. It is very difficult to break into a conversation between two people and may be seen as being rude. In the same way, avoid anyone who looks like they are engrossed in a deep conversation.

2. It can be a daunting experience to see a room full of people you don't know who all appear to be engaged in deep conversation. Take a moment just to look around; you will probably find either a group that you could ease your way into, or better yet, you may find another single person looking and feeling very awkward who is desperate for someone to come and 'rescue' them.
3. The best way to open a new conversation is by making a comment about the event itself. This makes it easy for the other person to respond. For example, you might say 'so what did you think about that last talk/session?'
4. From there, ask the person about him or herself. Make sure you listen and, when you have some common ground, it will be easy to build rapport.
5. Develop a short speech describing what you do. It is not enough just to say 'I'm a personal trainer'. There are people who will not fully understand what that entails or they may have preconceptions about what that is. Also, people buy benefits; in other words, they may hire a personal trainer, but actually they are buying what that personal trainer can bring to their life. For example, they might want to have more energy and feel better, and that is what they will hire you for. Being able to describe this neatly and succinctly will be useful to you in formal and informal networking situations. Keep your description down to 30 seconds and design it so that people are attracted and want to know more. Make sure you describe a typical issue that people have around their fitness and how that impacts their lives, then explain how you offer a solution and how that then benefits your clients.
6. Use business cards wisely. Take control of the situation by asking for a person's card, then asking if it is alright if you call them the next day, the next week or whenever – be specific. By asking permission, you will have set up an expectation in the other person and your call will be welcome.
7. As soon as you can after the event, write a couple of details on the back of the card, such as where you met, anything memorable about them and when you said you would call. By remembering details of the conversation, you will make the person feel special and important to you. Always make sure you call when you said you would.
8. By all means give your card too, but make sure you get theirs first. That way you will never have to sit around waiting for the phone to ring or risk losing a potentially valuable contact.
9. If someone does not want you to call, don't! A short card saying how nice it was to meet them will help you come across as thoughtful and well organised. You never know when they might be looking for a personal trainer in the future or when someone might ask them if they know of a good trainer. Even if someone is not interested in your service just now, make it your business to always be professional and pleasant because you never know what might happen in the future.

Building a brand

Think about some of the major brands in health and fitness and then think about how you recognise them and what those brands mean to you. You may not think that branding is relevant in the field of personal training, but branding makes you recognisable to your customers (by using a logo, name or corporate colour) and also communicates a feeling about you and the service you offer. You cannot ignore this because, without even trying, your business will be branded. The question really is whether you want to play a positive and proactive part in the brand-building process; remember, it is far better to be in control of every aspect of your business than to let it run you.

What is a brand?

Much more than your logo and colour scheme (although that is how you might be recognised), your brand is almost like your or your company's personality. It is an amalgam of perception and emotions that together lead to an identity and a value. A brand communicates your company ethos and principles. For example, think about a brand like Starbucks. They have a huge identity and presence and you can probably picture their logo and coffee-house style. However, they also do a lot to build themselves up within local communities (even though they are a global brand) by working with local schools and having local notice boards in their cafes. Innocent Drinks also build their brand by creating an emotion and a very particular funky/hippy style. They are environmentally aware and also contribute to charities that help the homeless, older people and so on. Their website and newsletter clearly indicate their ethos. It may well be that these aspects of the Innocent brand prompt a buying decision by the consumer just as much as their drinks. It takes time to build up this kind of image and for people to know what you are about.

How will a brand help you and why should you spend so much time on it?

The UK churns out a huge number of newly qualified personal trainers every year, so there are an awful lot of people all calling themselves personal trainers. By branding yourself and your company, you can make yourself stand out from the crowd. A brand can quickly and easily help a potential client to decide to call you rather than the next personal trainer. If you think about the example above, you may choose an Innocent Drinks smoothie over another because they use as much recycled plastic as possible in their bottles and you agree with that principle. As a personal trainer, a prospective customer might choose you because you have branded yourself as someone who contributes to your local community by offering free walking sessions in the park on Tuesday afternoons, for example. A brand will help to build confidence in your service so that your potential clients believe you will deliver exactly what you say you will. Your brand may make people feel that you are 'in tune' with them, that yours is a company they feel good about and can see themselves being a part of. We know that people buy emotionally and a brand's character can strongly influence buying decisions. Over time, a brand helps to build customer loyalty as you become a constant presence and a trustworthy source in an industry that is rapidly moving and can be seen as quite fickle.

10 steps to building a brilliant brand

1. Your service

Take a good look at your service. How do you operate? What message do you want to convey? What do you deliver well and what are you able to deliver consistently? Think aspirationally here. Think about the sort of service you would like to deliver, over and above what you do already. Think about what your customers would like in an ideal world. What would you like from a personal trainer?

2. Your client base

Once you have done some thinking, start to look at your existing client base. Are they the sort of clients you want to be working with? Who is your ideal client? Unless you have a clear picture of what you want, you will continue to get what you already have or what you don't want – if you don't know what sort of holiday you want but give it no thought, just shut your eyes and book 'a holiday', you may well end up in the very place you hate! Don't allow that to happen to your business. With your potential client in mind, start to think specifically about what they would like and what they wouldn't like. As personal training can be a lonely job, it is a good idea to ask some of the people in your life this question – but only if they fit your ideal client profile.

3. Get real

After all that thinking, you need to find out exactly where you are right now in terms of the type of service you offer and what your current and prospective clients feel about your business. Here you are looking specifically for words of feeling, or words that convey emotion, such as friendly, caring, inspiring, expensive and so on. Without asking, it is hard to know the answer to this question. We rarely get to know exactly how other people feel about us. These words will help you build your message.

4. How well is your business perceived?

Flowing from the last point, you need to find out how well your business is viewed by clients and potential clients. Are they clear about exactly what your service does for them? Do they trust you? How do they feel when your business is mentioned? It can be hard to get an honest answer on this one, but it is crucial to know, as a perception of poor value or quality could seriously damage your business and your potential to grow.

5. 'Brand stretch'

You need to assess your 'brand stretch'. This is about adding another business under the same brand that is outside the core business of the original brand. So, for example, you sometimes find charities these days that bring out a credit card offering under the same charity name or brand. The credit card is not part of the core business of the charity, but does provide a way for the charity to increase its income. In business, the Virgin brand is probably the one that has been stretched the most. The red and white logo can be found on anything from cola drinks to trains to music to financial services to gyms.

Start off by considering how you can grow your existing offer without moving too far away from your core business, but by offering something other than personal training to increase your income and level of customer care. For example, you could start to think about your clients even when they don't expect it by sending birthday cards or postcards while you (or they) are on holiday. You could offer workshops or social events. However, do be careful not to 'stretch' too far. If you dilute your core message too much, you may not be successful. You need to think about where your strengths lie and not enter into new ventures just because they are the latest thing. A few years ago, McDonald's tried to get into the travel and hotel business. They set up a hotel and train in Switzerland, but within a short time sold up because it didn't work. Their core business of selling fries and hamburgers does really well, but it did not translate well into another industry.

6. Create a congruent message

This means that your core competencies and brand values must marry up with your clients' – and, if appropriate, your employees' – perceptions. Take the time to fully figure these out, in addition to perceived quality and brand stretch, as mentioned above.

7. Communicate your brand message to the market place

Once the process above has been carried out, you are ready to communicate with the market place. Your brand 'message' must be central to everything about your business. So, starting with the point before your potential clients actually get to you, everything they hear and see about you and your service should scream out your brand message. This means all your literature and your logo should reflect the feelings and values associated with your message, and you should only advertise in publications that reflect your message.

8. Reflect the brand message at all times

Any contact made with you (or your staff) should reflect your brand message as well. Think here about the concept of 'moments of truth' (Carlzon, 1989). This phrase refers to every time any customer or potential customer comes into contact with any aspect of your business. In every moment, no matter how large or small, your 'brand' and therefore your business is created. This can be a make or break moment. A moment of truth can be a moment of magic or misery. If you work alone, this means you cannot afford to have an 'off' day. If someone rings to enquire about your service and you are in a bad mood and possibly a little 'off' with the individual, you have no idea how many times your business will now be painted in a very bad light. That person may well decide that you are not the sort of person they want as a personal trainer, and they may also tell their friends, family and so on. Similarly, if you are late for a first appointment with a new client, they may not come back to you for a second session. So, to this end, you need to think about your message with every professional interaction, from the message you leave on your answerphone to the car you drive. Everything about you communicates your message. That is why you cannot *not* communicate a brand; without you even realising, you already have a brand.

9. Review your brand regularly

Your brand should be a living thing. Once it is created, you need to regularly review it and decide whether you are sending out a congruent message to the world. For example, if you originally set up your business to work with elite athletes and all of your branding communicates that message, but six months later you find that you seem to be working much more in corporate health and wellness, you will need to alter the message you are sending out. You may make a conscious decision to change the focus of your business and, if that happens, you need to re-visit your branding.

10. Consistency, consistency, consistency

Remember to review everything in your business on a regular basis. This includes:

- your business name
- your slogan
- your logo
- your stationery style and quality
- location of workouts
- your advertising
- your body language and appearance
- your behaviour.

Regularly ask your clients if your brand message is current and if it mirrors their experience of working with you, as well as their needs and expectations. Similarly, it is a good idea to ask ex-clients and to really listen to their feedback as this can give you some really important clues as to where you are going right or wrong.

Cost-effective marketing materials

The section above on marketing is clearly crucial to your business; however, it would be very easy to be dismissive about it and think that you 'can't afford' to create a strong brand. Most personal trainers do not start off with huge marketing budgets, but you can create a very effective brand on a budget just by paying good attention to the detail of the materials you do invest in. So, what are the absolute essentials? A business card, a promotional leaflet and a good starter pack for new clients are probably your most important marketing tools.

It is worth spending money on getting these basic tools right from the start. Even if you have no other materials, these few will speak reams about your business, as you have seen above. A cheap card from the machine at the station looks like just that, has 'cheap' written all over it and will be associated with a cheap or low-quality personal training service. Rightly or wrongly, this will be people's perception. Instead, employ a graphic designer to create an image and possibly a logo that you are happy with. Choose colours that are in line with your brand message and get materials properly proof-read before you go to print. Once you have laid out for the basics, you will hopefully not have to spend anything else on them for some time. Your image and colour(s) will mean that people can immediately recognise you.

Testimonials are a very effective and cheap (or free) way of getting potential clients to focus on your brand and the benefits people might get from working with you. Ask some of your favourite or most successful clients to write a short testimonial for you and make sure you get their permission to use it. This is a hugely effective marketing tool as it shows people what they could get in their lives if they take on a personal trainer – specifically, you! Use these testimonials in any leaflet you produce.

To enable your clients to buy more from you, they have to know what is available. Create a 'menu' of the full range of products and services that you offer, including all the benefits your clients will gain from purchasing these. You can then use this in any brochures or leaflets you produce, on your website, with your letters or displayed in your studio or gym. Make sure that at some point you ask your clients to take a look through and see if there is anything else that might be of interest to them.

Give your business card a lot of thought. A smart one will make a big impression. Why not put a 'menu' of your services on the back? Using colour and even putting your photo on the card can all make it stand out from the norm.

These days, it is very important that you have web presence as this is often the first place people look. Getting your website designed and also noticed is an art form in itself and it would be a good area to spend money on getting an expert's help. Include your profile (and any other trainers who might work with you), your mission statement, your menu, frequently asked questions, testimonials, fitness tips and offer a free newsletter (which must come out regularly). This will help to spread your name, add extra value and increase your mailing list of potential new clients.

Create a 'welcome pack' for new clients. It is really nice for your clients to go away with something tangible when they have purchased a service. It creates a sense of added value and also ensures your clients have everything they need. Use a nice printed folder, perhaps using your logo and colours. Included in your pack might be your mission statement, information leaflet, your profile, menu of services and benefits, testimonials, terms and conditions, price and information about how to pay.

Speaking, writing and networking are all really effective. You will soon become known as the expert in your area if you make the effort to get out there and build your visibility.

LOOKING AFTER YOUR CLIENTS

In this chapter you will:
- discover the importance of safety for your clients
- learn the importance of risk assessments and how to carry them out
- understand the ethics of being a personal trainer
- discover the value of great customer care
- learn how to look after your clients to world-class levels
- perfect your communication skills.

Client safety

This is the most important aspect of personal training and probably the one that gets the least attention. Not only do you want to look after your clients' safety from your personal point of view, but ethically it is important that we are seen as a professional, caring industry. In addition, if you want to work with medically referred clients, your attitude to client safety will determine how clinicians view you. Finally, we do live in an increasingly litigious society and not only do you want to avoid such conflicts, but should such a situation arise you will need to prove that you did everything in your power to prevent accidents happening.

As a personal trainer, you should:

- Be and remain first-aid qualified. You only need to re-take your first-aid qualification every three years, but a lot can be forgotten in that time so do not get complacent about your ability to cope in an emergency situation. Make sure you practise your first-aid skills on a regular basis. If you are attached to a leisure centre or health club it will be easy to do this as you can always tag on to regular staff training and practice sessions. If you work alone, it is even more important that you practise your first-aid skills but less likely that you will, so try to find some way of practising or attending update training. If that is not possible, at least take a look through your first-aid manual on a regular basis. Just imagine how you would feel if an emergency occurred and you couldn't remember what to do.
- Always ensure you take detailed information before you start training a new client. A PAR-Q should be filled out at the very least, but many trainers like to ask more specific information about their clients. This may include some or all of the following, and you may wish to add more:
  - Do you have diabetes? (you may want to ask specifically about other medical conditions as well)
  - Are you pregnant or have you given birth within the last three months?
  - Have you had any surgery within the last six months?
  - Do you have any aches, pains or numbness?
  - Are you currently taking any medication?
- Ensure that you build a good relationship with your clients so that they feel able to chat to you easily. It is in casual conversation that you sometimes find out important medical information that may not have been revealed elsewhere.
- Make it clear to your clients how important it is that they let you know at the beginning of

your working relationship about any medical conditions they have and what, if any, medication they are taking. They will also need to let you know if and when conditions develop or change. You can write this into the contract, but also remind your clients by regularly asking them specifically about any medical conditions as well as how they are feeling generally.
- Should there be an underlying medical condition, always ask your client to see a doctor before they train with you.
- Never take on a client who has a medical condition that you don't understand or know about or, more importantly, if you are not competent to deal with it. This means that you need to be able to prove your competence in dealing with that specific medical condition, that is produce evidence that you know what you are doing. Qualifications or awards are a very good way of proving competence – it is not good enough simply to have the experience in a certain field. This is why membership of the Register of Exercise Professionals (see page 7) is so important; it is an unbiased organisation that has looked to national standards to state categorically what makes a person competent or not. Unless you are a doctor, physiotherapist or otherwise qualified person, you should never diagnose an injury or illness. The same applies to dietary advice and advice on supplements. By all means give general, good and sensible advice, but be very clear where to draw the line.
- Check how your client is feeling before every session.
- Make sure you have next-of-kin details for your clients and that you bring them to every session.
- Always carry a mobile phone with you when you are out and about training clients. Make sure you have charged the battery and that you have enough pre-pay (if that is your system) on your phone. Also, remember to check that you can actually get a signal wherever you are training.
- Ensure your client carries any necessary medication with them when training. For example, if you have an asthmatic client, make sure they have their inhaler with them at every session.
- Ensure all equipment is in good working order and never be blasé about safety when using weights or other equipment.
- Ensure that you always correct poor technique. This may sound obvious, but it is easy to get lazy.
- Have safety uppermost in your mind at all times so that you are constantly thinking ahead to what might happen, preventing accidents before they occur. This includes correct use of spotting techniques, among other things.

Risk assessment and accidents

A risk assessment is simply an assessment of anything in your workplace that could cause harm to people, followed by an evaluation of what precautions could be taken to minimise those risks. A risk assessment is a legal requirement in more formal work settings, but even if you work alone you should still carry out this exercise.

The first step is to identify exactly what the possible dangers are. For example, assuming you are not working in a gym setting, here is a list of possible dangers to you when working alone:

- parking your car in isolated or residential areas very early in the morning or after dark
- travelling alone
- working in clients' homes
- working in isolated areas with clients
- picking up, holding and putting down weights.

Five steps to risk assessment
Here are the five steps you need to follow for an effective risk assessment:
Step 1: Look for the hazards.
Step 2: Decide who might be harmed and how.
Step 3: Evaluate the risks and decide whether the existing precautions are adequate or whether more should be done.
Step 4: Record your findings.
Step 5: Review your assessment periodically and revise it if necessary.

Source: 5 Steps to Risk Assessment, *Health and Safety Executive (HSE), 1999*

Other dangers will become apparent in different situations, and you will also need to think about possible dangers to your clients. For example, if you are taking a client outside to train, it would be advisable to do a risk assessment on the area prior to the session taking place. The sorts of things you might think about include whether you can get a mobile phone signal and, if not, where the nearest phone box is, whether there is somewhere to leave valuables and whether there are any specifically hazardous areas such as a spot that is slippery underfoot. This way, you can take preventative measures where necessary and avoid emergencies occurring. Your risk assessment will include risks such as you or your client getting injured (see page 141 for a sample risk assessment form).

You then need to consider the likelihood of each risk actually occurring and how great the consequences would be. This will allow you to assess the level of attention you should give to reducing the risk and also the safeguards you need to put in place. Some safeguards are obvious and cost nothing, such as letting someone know where you are and what time you are expected to return when visiting a new client.

Should an accident or emergency occur, administer first aid and take all appropriate action. It is important to then write a report detailing everything factual about the event. This may be useful for any medic treating you or your client and it may also be useful at a later date should you need to recall the details for insurance or legal purposes.

Ethics

Many personal training and fitness organisations around the world have their own code of ethics or suggestions about how a personal trainer should conduct their business. If you sign up to a professional organisation, you may be bound by their code, but even if you do not, it is as well to integrate the following methods into your business as they are sound and will enhance your and your industry's professionalism.

- Be professional in all communication with clients and potential clients. This means looking well turned out and being prepared and early for each and every meeting. Equipment should be well maintained and calibrated regularly.
- Be rigorous about protecting client confidentiality. You will be given access to personal and often sensitive information. This is a privilege not to be abused under any circumstances. Confidentiality covers identity, personal information, conversations, behaviour and results.
- Ensure that you only practise in the areas in which you can prove competency. Never compromise a client's safety by accepting someone who has a medical condition you are not equipped to deal with or by using training modes for which you are not qualified. You would not go to a dentist to get your bunions sorted out, so do not insult

your clients' intelligence or harm their bodies by prescribing an exercise regime that is outside your scope of expertise.

- Continually update your education as a fitness professional. Keep up to date with new developments and concepts.
- Be honest and trustworthy in all your professional transactions. Integrity is vital to your professional credibility.
- Always show respect for clients and fellow professionals.
- Prior to any training taking place, agree goals and timescales with your client.
- Prior to any training taking place, agree terms and conditions with your client in writing.
- Operate within an equal opportunities framework. This means that all clients, potential clients, colleagues and professional contacts should be treated equally, regardless of age, colour, disability, sexuality, sexual preference, race or religion.
- Set clear boundaries and keep to them – personal trainers should never exploit the professional relationship with their client either sexually, emotionally or financially.
- Be sensitive to each client's comfort zone when it comes to the use of touch. Only touch your client after asking and if the use of touch will be beneficial in a particular exercise.
- Your highest priority is your clients' safety and welfare. This means that: any exercise prescription is safe and effective and that clients are shown how to safely operate any equipment or machinery; any recommendations for products or services are only made if they will benefit the client's health or well being and that no recommendations outside the trainer's scope of expertise are made (such as drugs, herbal remedies or banned substances); any recommendations (such as number of sessions or products) are only based around client need and not your financial gain; and that you take all reasonable steps to ensure a safe working environment.
- Ensure that your personal habits are congruent with your profession. This includes being a non-smoker, avoiding drug taking and maintaining a healthy diet and exercise regime. It goes without saying that you should never be under the influence of drugs or alcohol while training clients.
- Ensure you have adequate insurance cover (see pages 16–17).

Customer care

What does 'customer care' mean to you? Unfortunately, the term is bandied about so much these days that it all sounds rather dull, and most personal trainers don't really think about it or about their clients' experience of working with them at all. However, in an industry such as fitness the way you treat your customers is everything – yes, even more than what you know. Many businesses lose customers and never really know the reasons why. In fact, the majority of customers (around 96 per cent) who are unhappy with your service will never let you know. Most of them will simply not use your service again, but the damage can go much further as an unhappy customer will tell roughly 12 people about how awful your business is! (White House Office of Consumer Affairs, 1990)

Just think for a moment about how you like to be treated as a customer and what prompts you to make buying decisions in your life. We buy emotionally – that is, most of the buying decisions we make are led by emotion rather than need. Most of us have everything we need in our lives, but we choose to buy things based on a whole number of irrational choices. Your clients could achieve many of their fitness goals without your help; they just think they need you. Sure, you have a certain amount of technical information that can help your clients achieve their goals more quickly, but in truth, if they had the willpower and a strong enough desire, they could get by on their own.

Chip R Bell and Ron Zemke describe caring and competence as the two most important aspects of high-quality service (Bell and Zemke, 1989); how true and how simple. Think about examples of poor service you have received in the past, in any situation or industry. What was missing? Undoubtedly, it was one or both of those two things. But if you break it down to something so simple, then why is it so hard to achieve? Surely, part of this is about consistency: finding that smile and that 'go the extra mile' attitude despite your own feelings or mood. This, then, is the struggle for all of us in delivering exceptional customer care to everyone all the time.

Kristin Anderson and Ron Zemke describe the way that customers evaluate service quality on five factors: reliability, responsiveness, reassurance, empathy and tangibles (Anderson and Zemke, 2002).

Reliability

Customers expect that the information you offer is accurate and up to date and that you will deliver the service you said you would. Reliability is about keeping your promises as a service provider. When you make a promise to your clients, you must keep it. If part of your service is to send out a newsletter every month, then being reliable means doing just that – not skipping a month because you were too busy.

Responsiveness

Responsiveness is similar to reliability, but is based around the issue of time, that is how quickly you respond to your clients. They will expect you to always show up on time, to always invoice at the same time each month and to always do what you say you are going to do, *when* you said you were going to do it. By the way, why is this last one such a problem? Why don't people just do that? This comes down to business integrity. A client must never be kept waiting; there are very few real excuses for being late. Always leave enough time between appointments to allow for the unexpected. Always build in time for a traffic jam or for the train to be delayed. If you always have something with you to do (reading material or your mobile phone and your diary so that you can catch up on calls), being early will never be a problem for you either!

Reassurance

It is not enough to rely on 'teeth and eyes', in other words a great smile and a bubbly personality, to deliver exceptional customer service. Your clients need to feel safe and that they are dealing with a skilful, knowledgeable professional. By all means know your product (the technical skill of personal training), but also know your industry. Be up to date with new ideas, styles and innovations. Be clear on industry standards. Your clients will want to feel that you know how to solve their problems.

Remember, though, that this is not about having all the answers; as you will see in Chapter 10, it is about knowing how to elicit the answers from your client so that they become their own expert. The problem-solving aspect is not about you being the expert, but rather it is about you being the enabler and knowing you can help your client to reach their goals.

Empathy

This is a key skill for personal trainers and is critical in building rapport (see pages 56–9), but many instructors and personal trainers find it difficult to master. People in the fitness industry tend to be a certain 'type' – generally slim, smiley, fit and positive – and many find it hard to relate to people who are overweight, ill, unfit, have a dislike of sports and so on. However, it is your ability to relate to and empathise with clients, whatever their shape, size or attitude to exercise, that will help to build their confidence both in themselves and in you.

You need to be very clear about the difference between empathy and sympathy. Clients can have a lot of emotion attached to their physical state and you need to be able to understand and acknowledge those emotions (empathy) without taking them on yourself or agreeing with the client (sympathy). There is a big difference: empathy will ultimately be more supportive and elicit more change for your client than if you simply sympathise with them. Sympathy is what friends give and, other than give you a symbolic hug, it doesn't necessarily help you to move on.

For example, suppose you have a client whose husband died eight years ago. Within the first two years, she put on four stone in weight and has not managed to shift it since. Now, six years later she has come to you as a 'last resort'. Her story is that she has tried everything. As you spend more time with her, you notice that she uses the sympathy card a lot. She continually uses the fact that she lost her husband as a reason for anything that may not be right in her life, including her inability to lose weight. Grief is a tricky issue, and a sympathetic friend would agree with your client, listen for hours and never challenge her beliefs as otherwise they may risk the friendship. In comparison, an empathetic reaction would be to listen and to understand; to make it clear that you are on your client's side, but also to point out the reality of the situation. Her husband died eight years ago and she is responsible for her own life. Gently guiding this client to help her put her grief in the past and begin to move on will enable her to start seeing that the only person who can make her life better is herself. You can help her do this by showing her how to take control of her life by setting small achievable goals.

Case study

John visited a coffee shop in his favourite department store. After sitting down with his tray, he picked up the receipt and puzzled over it because a couple of the items were meant to be on 'special'. A woman who was clearing tables came over and asked if she could help. John probably would not have bothered to query the bill, but happily explained the situation to the woman. She offered to take the receipt over to the counter where he paid and checked it for John. She came back a moment later and told him he was completely right, he had been overcharged and the cashier would be coming over to give him the balance.

It is this hands-on approach that wins customers every time. Not only did the assistant notice an expression on the face of a customer, but she was then proactive in investigating the problem. She went out of her way and beyond the remit of her job (clearing tables) to not only satisfy but to 'wow' the customer. Going above and beyond what your customer would normally expect, not just satisfying but 'wowing' your customers, will ultimately win you more business than your competitors.

Top tips for delivering great customer care

1. Always put your client first.
2. Do what you said you were going to do, when you said you were going to do it.
3. Deliver your promise and then some. In other words, over-deliver; offer your clients more than they expect from you.
4. Get the basics right. In essence, there is no point in putting the frills on your service or going the extra mile if you have not got the fundamental basic product right. This means showing up on time, every time and delivering great personal training programmes that work.
5. Design quality systems within your business so that you are always organised and efficient (see pages 22–6 for more on this).
6. Work on being consistent in your delivery of exceptional customer service. It is no use being at the mercy of your moods.
7. Develop a fantastic attitude that will carry you through every situation. This is not as easy as it sounds, but there are plenty of resources at your disposal such as books, films, CDs and personal development courses. You need to keep yourself positive because that is what your clients need and expect of you. Focus on the positive and on winning. Create unstoppable belief in yourself and in your clients.
8. Be friendly and personable as well as professional.
9. Find different ways to communicate with your clients in between your sessions, such as e-mail, text, postcard, phone, fax (to the hotel when they are on holiday), books and CDs.
10. Incorporate an element of fun and play into your work. In the book *FISH!* (Lundin et al., 2000), the writers describe how a fish market in Seattle developed itself into a worldwide phenomenon by using very simple but strikingly effective customer-focused techniques. One of those techniques was to create 'play' in the workplace so that people had fun: if people have fun when they come to you, they will stay with you. Personal training can be a very serious business for a lot of people, but it doesn't have to be. As adults we sometimes lose the ability to play, but the fun that can be derived from play can be priceless when it comes to getting people fit and keeping clients!
11. Listen to your client's needs and be adaptable. If you have planned a particular session but when you turn up your client is tired, hungover, sad or otherwise predisposed to a different type of session, then change your plan. Be responsive to your client at all times.

To summarise, sympathy says the person is 'justified' in quitting, giving up hope and refusing to get help; empathy means putting yourself in the other person's shoes because you've been in similar situations and can show them how to survive it and move on. Empathy says there is no excuse for not continuing to work on the problem and do your best. It says you understand but don't accept the status quo. Quite a difference!

Tangibles

This is what your clients expect in terms of your appearance and the items you use, from your pen to the state of your car.

Assess your service now on what you think your clients expect of you in each category. Relate each section to your business as a personal trainer and what your customers expect. Putting yourself in your client's position is the easiest way to notice areas where your customer care skills could improve.

Communication

It is a shocking statistic that only 7 per cent of our communication is through the words we use, 38 per cent is through the tone we use and a whopping 55 per cent is via our body language (Mehrabian, 1981). Now the truth about this statistic is that, although often quoted, it is not actually the whole truth. These figures are based on situations where heightened emotion is involved, not general, everyday communication. However, it is still a useful way of illustrating just how little of what comes out of your mouth actually contributes to your ability to communicate effectively. The quality of your voice, the tone you use and how you use your body are all things you can and should focus on if you are to be a truly stunning communicator – which will be a great advantage when it comes to getting and hanging on to clients.

Communication is a skill like any other and should be practised with as much diligence as your technical skills. The ability to truly be 'with' your client is one that will pay dividends many times over.

Body language

Be aware of your body language. There is much debate about this topic: if you fold your arms, you could be seen as creating distance between yourself and your client; you could look aggressive or bored; or the reality may be that you are just cold! You must make up your own mind and act appropriately, but being aware will make a difference. For example, if you stand square on to your client instead of side on, you will send out messages of interest and attentiveness.

Congruence

When the words you use, the tone of your voice and your body language are all in alignment, this is known in NLP (Neuro-Linguistic Programming: a discipline concerned with the relationship between thought, communication and behaviour) as a 'congruent' message. This makes you and what you are saying more credible and believable. Conversely, an 'incongruent' message – often known as a mixed message – leaves the person you are talking to confused and ill at ease; they won't actually believe you as, even though you are saying one thing, your body is saying the opposite. This does not necessarily mean that you are lying; it is a far more subtle message than that. You possibly don't even know that you are giving mixed messages.

For example, imagine that Pete wants to hire a personal trainer. He goes to meet a trainer who has been recommended to him and who listens to what Pete wants to achieve, finds out about him and his lifestyle and asks about previous exercise experiences. As the personal trainer says 'I can definitely help you reach your goals,' he shakes his head. In this situation, Pete would be likely to have severe reservations about whether the personal trainer really meant what he was telling him. He just wouldn't believe it – he may not quite know why, he may just have a nagging suspicion that something isn't right. If, on the other hand, the personal trainer had responded with a smile and had nodded his head as he told Pete he could help, there would have been no confusion in Pete's mind.

While it is important for you to be aware of the messages you give out, this knowledge will also help you to spot incongruence on the part of your clients and recognise where you have a lack of commitment. If you suggest that a client does a certain amount of exercise between sessions, you can learn to read whether their response means they are really committed to doing it or whether they are just saying what they think you want to hear. For example, they might say 'yes' but not actually look you in the eye, their tone of voice might be a bit vague and their body might be slightly angled away from you. You would therefore not expect them to do the exercise – they are saying 'yes possibly', but you know that isn't really what they mean. When you recognise this, you can then use questioning techniques to get the client to see their own incongruence and hence to build more belief in themselves and their commitments to a long-term healthy lifestyle.

For example, in the situation described above you need to uncover the hidden objection or obstacle. By challenging the incongruence immediately, your client will start to reveal what their unspoken reluctance is about. So, if you said, 'you don't look like you are committed; on a scale of 1–10, how committed are you?' or 'I'm not convinced you are going to get that done; how likely is it that you will do x?', a new level of honesty and accountability is possible. You can then ask further questions to encourage your client to find ways around the obstacles, such as 'what would take you to a 10 on the commitment scale as opposed to the 5 you are on now?'

Listening

How well do you listen? Have you ever stopped to think about it? Most of us only listen to 25 per cent of what we hear (Anderson and Zemke, 2002). Many of us think that we listen when it is blatantly obvious to everyone else that we do not. There are too many personal trainers who simply see their job as passing information on to their clients, whether or not they want it or have asked for it, but listening to your clients is actually far more important.

Listening is one of the most important skills you can develop, yet it is also the most difficult to work on because we all think we are good at it already. Being blessed with an ability to hear is half the problem – the assumption is that hearing equals listening, which is just a fallacy. Listening is a skill, and skills take time, effort and knowledge to develop. On our personal training courses we are formally taught how to carry out the business of training clients and in school we are taught how to read and write, but nobody teaches us how to listen.

Stephen Covey, author of the bestselling management book *The Seven Habits of Highly Effective People*, talks about 'seek first to understand' (Covey, 1999). This is the most critical skill, but most of us never really bother with it. We think we are listening, but in reality most of us are actually formulating our own response. Imagine two people talking – when one finishes, the other immediately answers. This can only mean that the other person has been busy formulating their answer rather than listening; if they had been listening, there would have been a gap before they began to speak. Some people don't even let you finish before they jump in!

Think about a common scenario in personal training, such as someone wanting to lose weight. If an individual has had a weight problem for many years, they are likely to have amassed loads of information about different diets, exercise, various weight-loss principles and, most importantly, how they personally have responded to their efforts to lose weight. In other words, they are probably an expert (of sorts). Your job as a skilled personal trainer is to assist the client in their efforts to lose weight. What you bring to this partnership is your technical expertise (for example, the client may be using out-of-date or incorrect information or information that is not useful for them) and your ability to help the client remain motivated throughout the process. If you listen to the client and treat them as an 'expert', the information they have about their previous attempts at weight loss will prove invaluable to you in your mission to find methods and strategies that will work this time. However, if you don't listen, you may well repeat methods that haven't worked for your client in the past, leading to another failure to lose weight and a dissatisfied client.

You can see from this example that the ability to listen is crucial to the client–trainer relationship. However, the trouble with 'soft' skills like this is that they are often the most valuable but least tangible of skills to learn. You cannot get a certificate (although this by no means diminishes the importance of it) and you cannot measure your effectiveness very easily either. There are courses you can go on, but pretty much you are left to your own devices to brush up on your skills on an ongoing basis. The tips in the box on page 55 are a great starting point.

Presentation

There are several reasons why it's important to think about your presentation. First, you are a role model for your clients – they aspire to be something like you, otherwise they would not have hired you. Second, if someone is paying you for your services and you want to be treated like a professional, you need to look the part. It is good manners and conveys a lot about you and your business.

Remember that good presentation not only applies to your personal appearance, but also to your attitude, every consumable item you use in your business and every piece of advertising or marketing you produce. If your website is never updated, if your car looks like a mobile rubbish tip, if you smell of cigarettes every time you go to train a client, you will be sending out negative messages about your business. In fact, these send out an incongruent message about your business, as discussed earlier (see pages 52–3). We don't always know why we lose clients, and often the things we don't say speak louder than the things we do. So, pay attention to the detail and realise that you will be judged on everything about your business, no matter how small or big these things might seem to you.

Case study

Brian was interested in martial arts. He had trained for years, but had moved house and had to find a new club. He turned up at the new club nice and early. The sensei (instructor) was outside. He was around four stone overweight with long greasy hair and was enjoying a quick cigarette before the class. Brian turned on his heels and never went back. How could this person have anything to teach him?

A similar situation occurred to a friend of his who trained at college. The sensei was great. He talked a lot about the spirituality of martial arts and the student enjoyed both the physical and mental discipline of training. She loved the 'spiritual' side and the integrity of it, and aspired to the lack of ego involved in being a true martial artist. However, there was this one major problem: the sensei was engaged to one of the students, but at the beginning of every academic year, with the intake of new students, he seemed to find himself a new 'girlfriend' on the side. Everyone knew about this except, of course, his fiancée. The student finally left the club because what the sensei was teaching in class was not reflected in how he lived his life, so she began to mistrust and lose respect for him.

The second case study is more about incongruence than presentation, but in both cases you can see how the way you are in your personal life can have a huge impact on how you are viewed professionally.

Top tips for effective listening

1. Remember people's names. How often are you introduced to someone and within seconds you have forgotten their name? Being conscious of someone's name ensures that you focus on that person from the outset and reminds you to continue listening, rather than thinking about what you are going to say next. When someone (in any situation) tells you their name, repeat it silently to yourself and use it as soon as possible out loud to reinforce it in your mind.
2. Be there. Have you ever found yourself thinking about what you are going to have for dinner or that new car you want to buy when someone is talking to you? Worse, have you ever done that while training a client? Well, you are not alone. The trick is to be present in every moment. Constantly remind yourself to give your full attention to your client and focus on what they are saying to you. Become fascinated by that person. Just turning up to a session is not good enough. Be aware that all this takes energy, but that consciously directing your energy towards your client can be a very powerful tool.
3. If you find your mind wandering to what you are about to say while your client is still talking, try changing your body position and re-focus on their words.
4. Never interrupt. No matter how tempting, always allow your client to finish speaking before you start.
5. Try not to impose 'solutions'. Use questioning techniques to ascertain answers to your client's questions.
6. Give regular feedback. Check your understanding by asking questions and then summarising at the end (reflective listening). Not only do these techniques make your understanding stronger, but they also signal to your client that you have been listening.
7. In his book *The Seven Habits of Highly Effective People*, Stephen Covey goes beyond 'reflective listening' (see point 6 above) and talks about 'empathic listening', which means fully comprehending how the other person is feeling. You can get an intellectual understanding of this from what a person is saying and their demeanour, but to feel what it must be like in their world is another matter altogether. It means being more intuitive and emotionally connected, rather than just listening. Imagine what it would be like to be with someone who you felt knew 100 per cent what you were feeling and, therefore, absolutely understood why you do the things you do or behave the way you do. If your clients felt this way about you, they would be very comfortable in your abilities as a trainer because they would feel completely understood. They would feel valued for their individuality. From your point of view as a trainer, your ability to truly listen on this level will enhance your skills at being able to prescribe the right type of programme at the right time. It will allow you to enjoy your client's company much more as you will feel a greater sense of rapport and will also let you choose the best psychological approaches to get your client working most effectively (see pages 125–7 for more on this). It does not necessarily mean you agree with the other person's view, just that you fully understand it.
8. Show that you care. Remember that your body also sends out signals about your listening. Make sure that you look directly at your client when they are speaking and use body language such as nodding or smiling to continually re-affirm your listening status.
9. Avoid distractions while you are listening. Eliminate as much background noise as you can, and never take a phone call while you are listening to someone – certainly not a client!

Top tips to look your best

1. Pay attention to your personal grooming. This goes beyond just being clean – although that is important too. It may sound obvious, but sloppy grooming *is* noticeable. You need to iron your clothes, brush your teeth, look after your hands and nails – you don't have to have weekly manicures and wear red nail polish, just keep your nails trimmed and clean! Training shoes should be clean.
2. Ensure that your hair is neat.
3. Make sure your clothes are suitable and appropriate for the activity. This also means ensuring that your style suits the situation or the personality of your client. For example, an older client might feel more comfortable if you are dressed quite modestly.
4. Pay attention to your posture and how you move. Our posture often belies our thoughts and can affect our mood. Think about it: if you normally cross your arms and avoid eye contact with people when you are angry, what would happen if you changed your posture the next time you felt that way? If you adopt an open posture and make a conscious effort to connect with people, it is very hard to feel angry.
5. Make sure that you never smell of alcohol. You need to think about how long alcohol stays in your system and be aware of your alcohol intake on your days off as well as when you are working. Remember that alcohol can leave a noticeable effect the morning after the night before; do not have a heavy drinking night the night before you are due to work with clients.
6. You don't always have to have the latest, most expensive version, but make sure that every consumable item you use in your business is clean, tidy and well looked after. For example, make sure your car is clean and tidy (inside and out) and that it is in good repair. Make sure that you do not use a pen that is chewed and bitten at the bottom. These things are simple, but just take a bit of attention. Small things can say a lot about your business!
7. Ensure that any marketing materials you use look professional and are well produced. Again, this is not about buying the most expensive materials, but about attention to detail. Several years ago, I received a leaflet through my front door about a workshop. The subject was one I was interested in, so I took the time to consider whether I should go. In the end, I made my decision based on the quality of the literature. It was a beautifully produced, colourful leaflet, but there were so many spelling mistakes in it that I thought if they don't pay attention to the detail in a leaflet, what will the quality of the workshop be like? My judgment might have been totally unfair and inaccurate but, nevertheless, that was my impression.

Rapport

Rapport is a way of developing a common bond between people. When you have rapport, you feel that you are on the same wavelength as another person and that you have a common understanding. Rapport is one of the most important keys to effective communication. Without it you are unlikely to be successful in any endeavour, let alone personal training where your business depends on making people feel comfortable. Rapport creates trust and understanding between people and allows you to see your client's point of view and appreciate their feelings, regardless of whether you agree with them or not.

Rapport is vital to your business as a personal trainer because if people like you and feel that you really understand and are interested in their world, they will keep coming back for more and will also recommend you to their friends and acquaintances. People's decision to buy your product or to work with you is based more on rapport than on your technical skills as a trainer. Without even realising it and without paying any attention to rapport building, many businesses lose millions of pounds every year due to lost custom.

Rapport is created when people feel the other person really understands them and, more than that, really knows what it is like to be in their world. When you meet someone for the first time, it takes time to establish common ground (something that links you together). If that moment doesn't come, you feel no rapport and quickly lose interest. It becomes difficult to converse. On the other hand, if you find out you are both obsessed by yoga, you will happily spend time chatting away about that and feel you have met a 'really nice person'.

To create rapport, clearly you must find the common ground. If you think about your friends, you probably like them precisely because they are like you in many ways. Anthony Robbins said that 'when people are like each other, they tend to like each other' (Robbins, 2001) and this is the essence of rapport. Obviously, you will not have lots in common with all your clients and potential clients, so you need to work on your skills in order to be able to build rapport even where you might not find it more naturally. Following are some methods you can use.

Matching and mirroring

Most people try to establish rapport by making conversation; they try to engage people in conversation in the hope they might find common ground. However, this is a lottery. Sometimes it works and sometimes it doesn't. Have you ever talked to a total stranger and within moments hit on a common topic and ended up in deep conversation? You talk for an hour and realise you have found a soulmate. However, you can equally spend an hour talking to someone and find nothing in common. NLP techniques (see page 52) enable you to build rapport without relying on conversation. One technique is known as 'matching and mirroring', which allows you to create common ground with another person by adopting a similar physical state. We know that body language plays an important part in communication (see page 52) and if you watch two people who are good friends or who are romantic partners, you will notice that they often adopt the same stance or posture when they are together. They move in a similar way, laugh at the same time and adopt a similar speech rhythm. In other words, they 'match' each other. It therefore makes sense that you can adopt a similar strategy – mirroring – to make someone feel more comfortable in your presence.

Mirroring works on a subconscious level to make the other person feel that you are similar in some way. To mirror someone, you need to observe how they use their body. You can focus on the big stuff, like their posture or the position of their arms or legs, but more subtle observations can be just as effective; you can mirror someone's facial expression, their hand movements, particular tensions in their body, the way their head is tilting, the position of their feet, their breathing pattern and so on. You can even mirror their tone of voice, the speed of their speech, their pitch and particular words they use. This is a skill worth mastering, but it needs to be done in a natural and unobtrusive way so as not to be obvious or insulting. If you do it subtly, people won't notice as most of the time their focus will be on themselves, not you.

In itself, matching and mirroring does not guarantee rapport and you will need to check the level of rapport you have reached. This can be done quite simply by starting to 'lead'. In other words, where you have been matching and mirroring the other person's movements, you now start to take the lead in changing your own posture and so on with a view to the other person following you (on an unconscious level). If they don't follow, go back to matching and mirroring. However, if they do follow, you know you have built rapport and you can start to use your leading to influence your client's behaviour. For example, if you have a new client who appears nervous or apprehensive, you can use leading to help them relax. You could adopt an open relaxed posture, preferably sitting down and leaning back, slow down your breathing and speech and smile.

When done with skill, mirroring can help you to feel what the client is feeling. Not only will the client feel a greater sense of rapport with you, but the feeling will go two ways. As you gain a greater understanding of your client, your level of empathy will also rise. Think of this as a way of 'listening' with your body.

Different ways of communicating

We all have preferred ways of communicating and perceiving the world. The three ways identified in NLP are visual, auditory and kinesthetic. These are simply preferred ways of understanding the immense amount of stimuli that enters our brains. People use all three ways to interpret things, but we each have one way that we prefer to use. This is the one we resort to when we are at our most relaxed and, when reflected back to us, is the one that will have the most effect. Once you understand someone's preferred sense, you can use this as another tool with which to create and build rapport.

Visual

Someone who is predominantly visual will 'see' the world. They learn best by watching first and succeed by creating mental images of what they want to be, do or have. As you speak to them, they will be creating a picture in their mind's eye. The language they use will be peppered with references to seeing. For example, they will 'see' what you mean; as you describe something, they will be able to 'picture' that; things will 'look' good to them and they will understand things 'clearly'. They will also speak quickly because they think in pictures, so their speech has to be fast to keep up with the images. Their speech can be higher in pitch and their breathing might be quite shallow.

You can see how having this knowledge will help you to understand your clients better and to get into their view of the world. For example, if you are not a visual person, your appearance or how your studio looks may not be something that is particularly important to you. In fact, you may not even notice if things are a bit scruffy. However, if you have a visual client they will certainly notice such things and may be put off your business. If you understand their view, you can pay attention to such detail, enabling them to feel more comfortable and in tune with you even though you don't 'agree' with the importance they place on such things.

Auditory

Auditory people listen to what is going on around them to understand and interpret information. They will 'hear' what you are saying, ask you to 'tell' them how to do something and tell you that something 'sounds' good to them. They might murmur to themselves when they are trying to solve problems. Their speech will be rhythmic and more deliberate than that of visual people as they are very aware of how their voice sounds. Their breathing will also be slower and deeper to match the voice.

Kinesthetic

Touch, emotion and 'gut instincts' are all important to kinesthetic people. They base their decision on whether to trust someone on whether they feel it is OK to do so. They will 'feel' this way about a certain topic, 'touch' base next week and will be unable to 'grasp' that. Their words will be all about touch, feel and emotion. Their speech will be slower as they need to access emotion or feeling in their responses and they may pause more than usual. Kinesthetics will be the most comfortable with touch and they may touch you on the arm or the back as they communicate.

Putting this into practice

It is easy to see how knowledge of these three types can help you not only to acquire more clients, but also to make your own clients feel more comfortable with you and thus stay with you for longer. You can also use the knowledge to teach your clients in the way that they will be most receptive to and that will make the most sense to them.

So, for example, a **visual** client would love to have their fitness assessment information and their progress printed out in bar graphs and charts, all in colour. They will feel that you understand them better if you speak quickly and use your hands as you are talking.

Auditory clients will appreciate music while working out and will enjoy listening to information on CD or cassette rather than having to read it.

Kinesthetics will respond well to the question, 'what do you feel you'd like to achieve this session?' and will want to touch or feel what it is like to use a new piece of equipment. Don't spend so long on explanations. Let them jump on straight away and then explain so they can feel what you are talking about.

Case study

Darren received a phone call from a prospective client and the conversation went something like this: 'Hello. I'm looking for a personal trainer and wanted to see what sort of service you offer. I'd like to get a picture of what you do. I've spoken to several trainers and have not made my decision yet because I'd like to get your perspective on how I should deal with my fitness,' and so on.

It was clear from the language used that the prospective client was a visual person, so Darren responded with such things as: 'All my new clients receive a fantastic red folder containing all the information they need and every three months they receive a colour print-out of their results' and 'You will be able to see results within the first month of working with me'. Needless to say, he got the business!

LOOKING AFTER YOURSELF

6

In this chapter you will:

- learn how to look after yourself while working
- learn how to keep yourself strong, healthy and positive every day
- learn how to deal with negative clients
- discover tools to help you find balance in your life
- learn how to manage your time more effectively
- learn how to manage the boundaries in the client–trainer relationship.

The best advert for your personal training business is always yourself. Unless you are a good role model for your profession, in that you keep yourself fit, healthy and positive, potential clients automatically mistrust you. People will come to you for many reasons, but on the whole they want to 'feel better'. Whether that means losing weight, gaining weight, looking better or having more energy, the outcome is the same. Therefore, you need to be a walking shop window for your services so your clients want to be like you! Another reason to look after yourself is that you need to in order to fulfil the requirements of the job. Far too many trainers start out enthusiastically, but within a couple of years find that they are exhausted and burned out. As most personal trainers are self-employed, there is a great temptation to just keep on working, fitting in more and more sessions and not taking a day off because you don't have any sick pay to rely on. While this might seem like a good idea at the time, you should not underestimate the toll it will take on your body in the long term. It can be incredibly stressful to feel physically unwell, but to feel compelled to work through it. Not only is this physically unsustainable, but it can lead to mental burnout and boredom as well. In short, make sure you look after yourself and build in enough of a contingency plan or a financial cushion to enable you to take time out when you need to – be it for sickness or holidays.

Learning how to look after yourself is an art and is not just a case of following the advice that you dish out on a daily basis, although that is part of it. If you accept the concept of 'holistic' health, you must look at your whole being and not just the physical side. Of course that plays a part, but for most trainers it is not the overriding issue. It is more a question of balance and learning to listen to your whole body system. A healthy social life and relaxation time are as important as training your physical body.

Here then are the top ways to look after yourself!

Diet

When you are running around between clients, in and out of a car or training back to back at the gym, you can sometimes neglect to look after your fluid and food intake, leaving you feeling weak and exhausted by the end of the day. Lack of water can have a devastating effect, not only on your energy levels but also on your concentration. Ensure you drink regularly by keeping your water bottle topped up and with you all day. It can be a good idea to drink several glasses before breakfast as this sets you up for the day. Also ensure that you have high-energy snacks with you so you are not dependent on whatever is available locally. In short, ensure you follow the advice you give to your clients.

Exercise

The problem with being a personal trainer, or indeed anyone in the fitness industry, is that your hobby becomes your work. This means that the way many people like to relax or revive themselves, that is sport or exercise, can become a 'busman's holiday'. In much the same way that some orchestral musicians get to the sad point in their lives (given that music would once have been an overwhelming passion) where they leave their instrument at work at night, personal trainers can find that their enthusiasm for physical activity dwindles and they can end up exercising only with their clients. For many reasons, this is, of course, completely inappropriate. Time spent with a client is *their* time, not yours. You need to be fitter than your clients in order to have the energy to train them, instead of simply training *with* them. However, sometimes we are so busy dishing out advice that we forget the most obvious points in relation to ourselves. Think about what you enjoy doing. What did you enjoy doing as a child that you don't allow time for now as an adult? Can you buddy up with someone and find yourself a training partner? Find some way of keeping exercise fresh for you. Also remember to keep your own exercise regime balanced; for example, if you are doing a lot of running with clients and also train yourself in the gym, you may need to do more balance or flexibility sessions such as tai chi or yoga.

Invest in your greatest asset – your body

Again, we often advise our clients to invest time and money into looking after their bodies, but fail to do so ourselves. Remember that if your body is not fit to work, your business will fail, so do whatever you need to do to keep yourself in tip-top condition. This may include some or all of the following:

- Invest in alternative or complementary therapies for the treatment and also the prevention of health problems. Massage, reflexology and acupuncture are just a few examples. It is worth taking the time to find good therapists (remember that this will have a knock-on effect as, if a therapist is good, you will be able to refer your clients on to him or her). If you cannot afford regular treatments, try suggesting a skill swap, where you give a therapist personal training sessions in exchange for sessions with them. Many of these treatments not only help to prevent injuries, but they also help to balance energy levels and keep the body in top condition.
- If you have a lot of clients and are training on most days of the week, you should own several pairs of training shoes and rotate them so that you never wear the same pair for two days running. This allows time for the trainers to breathe and completely dry out, thus avoiding many of the foot problems associated with prolonged sports shoe use. In addition, ensure you renew your trainers frequently so that you always have enough suspension and protection for the foot. A good rule of thumb is that as soon as your trainers are so comfortable you almost feel like you aren't wearing any, it's time for a new pair.
- Staying with feet, pedicures and regular sessions with a chiropodist not only provide

valuable care for your very precious feet, but also some rest and relaxation – it literally forces you to put your feet up and relax!

Rest and relaxation

No-one can keep going at full pelt for long periods of time without burning out. The business of personal training can be emotionally and physically demanding and, unless you pay attention to your own ability to relax and unwind, you will soon find you have nothing left to give. Make sure you schedule down time on a weekly basis.

Bear in mind that there is a difference between conscious and subconscious relaxation. For example, you might feel relaxed when you watch television, but watching television actually raises the heart rate and does nothing to induce a relaxed state. This arousal comes from the flashing lights and constant noise, but also from negative messages. That is not to say that all unconscious relaxation is a waste of time; just be careful about the activity you choose. Generally, as long as it is different enough from what you were doing previously (in this case training clients), unconscious relaxation can be very rewarding. So, playing with children in the park or going for a meal with friends are all great ways to relax. Conscious relaxation would include things like meditating, getting a massage or attending a yoga class. Silent meditation is, of course, the best form of relaxation as it removes all stimuli and helps your body heal itself.

Also, make sure you take time for holidays. Many trainers fall into the trap of not taking enough breaks, especially if they are self-employed. When you are not working, you are not being paid and that can be stressful in itself. However, you will just be storing up problems if you don't take adequate time out for yourself – people who take holidays generally experience lower levels of fatigue and are less worried and less irritable than people who don't.

Energy management

Energy management is a key issue for most people today. In fact, most of your clients will be trying to find their own solution to this problem and will probably look to you to help them sort it out! You might think that if you look after yourself with all the tips we have talked about in this section, you will have loads of energy. To a certain extent this is true, but it really is only a part of the story. The ability to have and maintain copious amounts of energy is a subtle one. The more you become aware of it, the more sensitive you will become to the things that affect your energy balance, be that positively or negatively. As with most sections of this book, an entire book could be written on this subject alone. I have boiled it down to a few key areas to be aware of and made recommendations for further reading (see pages 147–9).

Avoid negative people

Have you ever noticed the toxic effect some people have? I once heard them called 'psychic vampires' and this is an apt description. These are the negative, whinging, whining people who seem to blame everything and everyone else for their circumstances and who go through life complaining and moaning. They like nothing better than to dump on you and drain you of the energy they know you have. You only need to spend five minutes in their company to feel exhausted and negative yourself.

'Psychic vampires' often don't know that they are so negative or that they have such an effect on the people around them. Unfortunately, some of these people will be your clients and will use you as a shoulder to cry on. They will come away feeling much better, but you will just feel exhausted and wonder why, or what you can do about it. The best way to prevent people like this sapping your energy is to try your best to avoid them or, if they are clients and you cannot avoid them, at least limit your time with them. If this is not possible, you could gently steer the talk away from the negative and refuse to engage or indulge in that kind of conversation. Keep the conversation strictly around physical activity and what you are doing in the session to help them remain focused.

Making people aware of just how negative they are is good, but potentially quite difficult in a trainer–client relationship, and there are other ways to protect yourself. Watch your own self-talk before going into sessions with such clients. You will probably find that there is a fair amount of trepidation and anxiety if you know you have a 'difficult' client coming up. However, the more you build it up in your own mind, the more the client will drain you even before their session begins. Instead, try to go into the session with a strong state of mind and visually imagine a boundary between you and them that will allow the good stuff (your training and your positive energy) out, but won't allow their negativity in – imagine it bouncing off you or going over your head. Making a mental decision beforehand not to take things personally or let them affect you can have striking results, and you may even start to see a change in your client too.

Another technique is to be pro-active in helping your client to behave in a more positive and confident way. This can be done by helping them to see things differently. So, for example, if they are discussing with you how they hate going out for a run on their own and how it is really difficult when you are not around, you might subtly suggest that their use of language could be the very thing holding them back. If they see this 'problem' as a challenge and imagine each block they run taking them closer to the image they really want for themselves, they might start to see that their automatic, negative view of the world is not always a helpful strategy for them in life. See this as part of the training session so that, over time, they stop draining your energy and start to 'get it' themselves.

Listen to your body

The more you start to listen to your own body, the more you will notice the effect that noise has on your energy levels. There is, of course, a difference between welcome and unwelcome noise, but even if you think about music you will realise the effect it can have on your emotions and energy. It is a strange fact that a higher proportion of orchestral conductors (compared with the general population) live a very long and healthy life (Rochlitz, 1993). Studies have been carried out that have clearly shown the marked effect certain music can have on people's moods and behaviour. For example, the 'Mozart Effect' is a phenomenon discovered in 1993 when a study in *Nature* concluded that students who listened to music by Mozart performed better in a spatial reasoning test than those who listened to other music or no music at all (Rauscher et al, 1993). Since then, there has been much interest in this area and CDs have been released that are said to affect mood and concentration in children and adults. Most of us are unaware of just how much noise affects us, but it can increase our heart rate and keep us so stimulated that it disrupts sleep.

De-clutter your life

Much has been written about clutter over the last few years and you may wonder what it has to do with you and your business, but just think about how your energy levels rise when you have had a good clearout. Whether you believe in such esoteric things as feng shui or not, just try it and see. Living and/or working in a cluttered environment not only makes you feel disorganised as you waste valuable time (and energy) searching for the things you need, but it literally saps your energy. And by the way, this refers not only to your physical environment, but also to your mental state. Make a master list of all the stuff you need to do. Just keep adding to it over a period of time. This will include all sorts of things, large and small, such as clean the car, replace sticky fluid corrector, call Dad, buy birthday present for so-and-so, etc. This list is endless. It is important that you include all those little niggly things that really get on your nerves, but you never quite get round to doing. The problem with these things is that every time you get to them, (for example every time you get into your messy, untidy car) your energy is drained. It fills up your head with mental clutter. Once you have that master list, attempt to take something off it every day. Some items literally take seconds to sort out!

Diet

Much of our diet is toxic and can have profound effects on our energy levels. For example, coffee and other stimulants may be good at giving you short bursts of energy, but these will inevitably be followed by energy slumps; in the same way, a diet high in sugar will provide brief energy highs followed by slumps. Similarly, any habit-forming substances should be avoided where possible. It goes without saying that smoking is probably one of the worst things you can do to your body and should be avoided at all costs.

Finding balance

There are many ways to focus on the amount and quality of sleep you get and also to build relaxation into every day. However, one of the most obvious areas where personal trainers can suffer is in their own scheduling of appointments. Because we want to create great customer service, love our job and our clients and don't want to turn down work, we often find ourselves booking too many early morning and late evening appointments. Paying attention to this and ensuring you sometimes allow for more sleep time can make the difference between burn-out and exhaustion and firing on all cylinders. Make sure you plan out your week, paying attention to all aspects of your life. This will include your own fitness, health and wellbeing (whatever those needs are for you) as well as your relationships and family commitments. When you work for someone else, it is very clear when you are working and when you are not; the danger for personal trainers who are self-employed is that every hour of every day is a potential working hour. Be clear about when you want to work and when you don't. Plan how many hours you want to work and when those hours will be. Keep in balance and don't allow your desire to please your clients override your needs to live a happy and fulfilled life. It can be helpful to take an inventory of where you stand in all aspects of your life. Use the life balance chart on page 66 (see Figure 6.1) to list all the areas of your life and plot how well you feel they are going. These might include fitness, health, relationships, social life, family, religion or spirituality, finances, self-development, career/business, partner and home. You need to decide for yourself the important aspects of your life. Give yourself a score of 1 to 10 in each category based on one being really poor – you feel that

that area of your life is not going well – and 10 being absolutely amazing – things couldn't get any better. Don't agonise over it – do it quickly and without too much thought.

Figure 6.1 Life balance chart

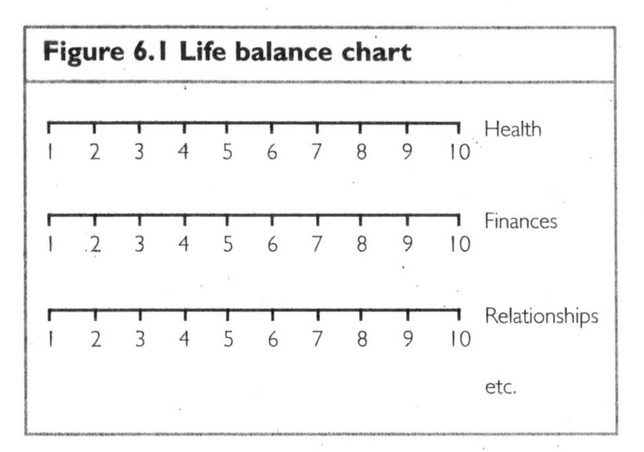

This will give you a snapshot of how your life is at the moment. It can often be quite telling and will show the areas of your life where you need to re-direct your energy. No-one is in balance all the time. There are periods when the work rolls in and you need to knuckle down and get on with it, but stay there for too long and your personal relationships will suffer. This lack of balance can lead to psychological as well as physical problems. Think of it as riding a bike. A beginner is constantly falling over. One only manages to ride by a constant correction of balance. For most people, these corrections are so subtle they don't realise they are doing it. In the same way, you need to keep yourself and your life in balance in order to stay upright.

Time management

Of course it is nonsense to think that we can manage time – usually time manages us! Everyone has just 24 hours in every day, and all we can do is manage ourselves within the time given to us. There are vast amounts written on the subject of time management, but there are some points that are particularly relevant.

If you are a person who is consistently late, you are probably unaware of what it does to your energy and stress levels, let alone the message it sends out to clients. Being late means you feel anxious and stressed, you end up apologising and making excuses and you generally feel out of control. The constant apologies undermine your confidence and your ability to feel professional and authoritative. However, to change the habits of a lifetime can be a challenging process.

In the same way, procrastination is almost as bad as lateness in terms of how it affects your psyche. William James said 'Nothing is so fatiguing as the eternal hanging on of an uncompleted task'. Anyone who tends to procrastinate will know just how true this is. Getting to the bottom of this issue is, again, a challenge.

Many of the problems associated with time management can be sorted out just by giving your schedule more forethought. We often make our lives much harder than we need to. For example, we may know that after giving a whole week of personal training sessions we feel drained and exhausted. Simply putting a day off into the diary after several days on the go may make all the difference. If you put it in as you book the work, you are not stuck doing the same thing you have always done and wondering why you feel drained or you never have enough time to take a day off. In the same way, putting your holidays into your diary or planner at the beginning of each year means you can be clear with your clients and give them lots of notice, as well as meaning you will definitely get the breaks you need.

On a more practical level, making time in your day for you is as important for you as it is for your clients. You need to take time out for lunch in order to be able to perform at your best. You need to create relaxation time or time to see your friends. If appointments and work commitments threaten this, start to use the tools you suggest to your clients – put this time in your diary, in ink. Learning to find the time for everything and finding techniques that work will make you a more effective and empathic trainer who understands just what challenges your clients face.

Learning to manage your time so that you fit everything in is an art and different things work for different people. Here are a few ideas to help you manage your time better.

Make lists

At the end of every day or the start of every new day, make a list of what needs to be done and prioritise it by whatever method works for you. You might do this by simply using numbers to indicate the level of importance, such as one for urgent and two for those things that it is not essential to do today. You could use colour and use red to highlight the things you have to get done urgently and blue for the less important things. Or you could split your page into topics, such as list who to phone, who to email, stuff to do, programmes to write up or desk-work to do. This can be a time-efficient way of organising your list because you can make all of your phone calls in one go rather than flitting between one task and another. Then tackle the hardest task first. This really does work. You have more energy at the beginning of a day and are less likely to let other things get in the way. Alternatively, write down just three things you commit to getting done that day. This is a great little tip for those of you whose 'to do' list seems endless and for whom every day feels like a failure because you never manage to tick everything off. This also forces you to focus on the most important things to do.

Learn to say no

Sometimes we are so busy trying to please everyone in our lives that we feel we can't say no. There are times when the word 'yes' has come out of our mouths before we've even realised we are doing it, and then we wonder why we feel overcommitted, overburdened and burned out. The next time someone asks you to do something, just pause before you answer and, if you feel an overwhelming urge to say yes, ask for a little time to think about it. In this way, when you get back to that person you can be ready and prepared to say no if you want to.

Don't always be available

With so many methods of communication, we often feel we need to be available to people 24/7. Whatever happened to taking the phone off the hook and relaxing in a nice hot bath? You would not (I hope) have your phone on while you were training a client, so why not give yourself the same level of respect by turning off your phone when you are busy? If you are trying to get a piece of work done, especially one that you would rather not be distracted from, it makes sense to turn off your phone for the duration. Interruptions to your flow can throw you off course for far longer than the actual call itself.

Get organised

Keeping your home, office, studio, etc in good order will save you untold amounts of time in searching for buried items. See pages 22–6 for more ideas on getting organised.

Don't put things off

Procrastination, as mentioned above, is one of the biggest challenges for most people and learning to deal with this is essential to your professionalism and to your self-development. If you are putting something off, break it down into smaller 'chunks' that are more manageable. Do what you can do now. In order to get started, set a timer of, say, 15 minutes and tell yourself you will do just that. Often, once you have started you will continue. Getting over that initial inertia is the hardest part.

Allow for the unexpected

Make 'holes' in your time. Only schedule 50 per cent of your time to allow for emergencies and interruptions.

Prioritise

Have you ever felt like you were really busy all the time and you couldn't possibly see yourself being organised or having enough time to fit everything in? Sometimes it is good to just take a step back and really look at how you spend your time. Most of us don't realise just how much time we waste doing things that are not really that important. Keep a time log for a week to see how you actually spend your time. You have to be careful here. It is very easy to forget the little things that really eat into your day. If you have ever worked in an office, you will know about the eternal argument that goes on between smokers and non-smokers. A few of those 10-minute 'ciggy' breaks a day easily add up to an hour. Over the course of a week, you could be looking at five hours; that's 20 hours or half a week off every month. That's a lot of time! Discipline yourself to see what is important and make that your priority. In the same way, there are some things you could just let go of and not do. There are some things that do not benefit us or anyone else and should just be dropped.

In order to be a role model to your clients, you need to get on top of the time management issue. As with every other behaviour change, whatever challenges you face in learning to organise your time, it will mirror the challenges some of your clients face in taking up the exercise habit. The lessons you learn from disciplining yourself will be useful in assisting your clients.

Finding inspiration and staying positive

Have you ever noticed just how much negativity there is in our world? The problem is that it is so insidious and inbuilt into our culture that we hardly even notice its existence any more. Just looking through any of our daily newspapers or watching the news is enough to bring your positivity crashing down. Our self-talk can also be negative. If we spoke to others the way we internally speak to ourselves, we wouldn't have any friends, let alone clients! Perhaps we need to start being a little kinder to ourselves and also start to replace some of that negativity with positivity to help keep us buoyant.

Maintaining a good attitude is challenging, but there are things you can do to counterbalance the stuff that is coming at you from the outside. Reading is something that you should do as a matter of habit. Most successful people read a lot. This could be technical training information or self-development books, but the more positive messages you send your brain the better. Listen to inspirational speakers and attend seminars and conferences that will feed your mind with the sort of attitude you want to cultivate.

Boundaries

It sounds obvious, but personal training is a personal business! You will get to know many aspects of your clients' lives in great detail. As you are there to support and train your client, they will often come to view you as a 'friend'. With some clients this can feel very comfortable. However, the need to keep things professional cannot be over-emphasised. Not only is this a requirement of many fitness organisations you may wish to join, but also if the relationship changes its definition it will compromise your value as a personal trainer. Think about how difficult it is to learn anything from someone you know. If you were taught to drive by a parent, you will understand the difficulties faced by trying to learn when the relationship is different from just 'teacher' and 'pupil'. In addition, forming a relationship with your client, especially a romantic partnership, could seriously undermine your status and reputation and could be seen as an abuse of your position. Once the damage has been done, it is very difficult to change perceptions. As you may grow to be a confidant of your clients and they may share personal information with you, they can feel confused by the limits of that relationship. In addition, as clients feel cared for and positive in your company, they may want more than you are able to or wish to give. It is up to you to develop the skills to keep the relationship on a purely professional basis, thereby protecting you, your client and the integrity of your relationship. Here are some tips to help you:

- Use touch only when trying to focus your client's mind or when demonstrating a particular exercise. Always ask for permission to touch and remove your hands as soon as possible.
- During sessions, keep the conversation on the business of personal training. Try to steer conversations away from the client's personal life.
- Never discuss your personal life with clients.
- If a client should suggest meeting up socially, politely refuse, making a credible excuse if necessary.

Personal safety

Many personal trainers make the mistake of not thinking about their personal safety until they come to meet their first client in the client's home, and suddenly realise what a vulnerable position they have placed themselves in. For others, the realisation may not come until either they or someone they know experiences an unpleasant or dangerous incident. The common thought that 'it will never happen to me' must be over-ridden as there are very real potential dangers associated with being a personal trainer. Here are some measures you can take to protect yourself when working:

- Always make sure you park under good lighting.
- Try to leave with your client and/or tell friends and family where you are, and arrange to call them at a set time. The Suzy Lamplugh Trust, the leading authority on personal safety, recommends setting up a permanent 'buddy' system whereby you always let someone know your daily schedule, including details of all appointments. Make sure that your buddy has full contact details for all the clients you train in their homes.
- When meeting clients for the first time, always arrange to meet them in a public place rather than their home. A coffee shop or a gym would be ideal.
- Carry a mobile phone with you at all times.
- When giving a new client your contact details, do not give your home address.

PART THREE

TRAINING YOUR CLIENTS

ASSESSMENT AND GOAL SETTING

7

In this chapter you will:

- learn how to carry out effective first meetings with prospective clients, including how to lead the conversation
- discover what questions to ask to ensure you get all the information you need and that you win the business
- decide whether or not to assess your clients' fitness
- learn how to help your client to set powerful goals and give them the tools to stick with them.

The first meeting

Your relationship with your clients does not begin when they hire you; it begins when they first contact you. This is why it is so important to get absolutely everything right, as discussed in Part Two: from adverts to phone calls, potential clients will be weighing you up and deciding whether or not they want to work with you. For this reason, you should never take on a new client before meeting up with them. In this chapter, we will address the reasons why you need to do this and the key questions you need to think about before you meet up, in order to get a favourable outcome for both you and your prospective client.

Why should we meet?

When you find a prospective client, it is important to consider whether you are right for them as a personal trainer and whether they are right for you as a client. Don't fall into the

Case study

Jack worked as a personal trainer in a gym. He had recently qualified and was eager to take on more clients to supplement the wages he received working on the gym floor. So, when a member asked for personal training sessions, Jack obliged. After completing a brief lifestyle questionnaire, they got on with the business of training.

The client, Daniel, was 62 years old and suffered with arthritis. This was particularly bad in the hip area and sometimes caused him to walk with a limp, but he was otherwise healthy and keen to have a tailor-made programme to keep him fit into his old age. However, Jack had no experience of working with older adults, had not taken any training courses in working with older adults and, in short, ignored the problem of the arthritis entirely. The programme he gave Daniel included a simple weights routine that he could do on three days of the week, preceded by 20 minutes running on the treadmill.

After two months of training, Daniel found the pain in his hip was becoming unbearable and on the advice of his doctor he had a hip replacement operation. Luckily for Daniel, he found that after his recovery he could no longer muster up enthusiasm for the gym and dropped out. I say luckily because, although Jack's exercise prescription did not cause Daniel to have the hip replacement, running could certainly have aggravated the arthritis. Worse, Jack had failed to meet his client initially and identify first if there were any other underlying health issues his client might have had and second whether he was competent to deal with this particular client. If Daniel had gone back to his exercise programme and Jack had unwittingly prescribed, say, strengthening work for the adductors, bringing the leg across the body, he may have caused more damage and could have been facing a legal situation.

trap of taking whoever comes along without any discrimination; this could lead to you feeling uncomfortable or unhappy in the relationship, the client not achieving results and, at worst, having a lawsuit filed against you for negligence (if you were to take on someone who had a medical condition in which you could not prove competence).

At any rate, it is good practice to ensure that you can offer what the client is looking for. Think about it: on most occasions when you hire someone for any reason, you prefer to meet them first to see if you get on, or if the person is up to the job. Why should personal training be any different? Even if a person were willing to take you on just from seeing your advert, you would be unwise to do so without meeting them first.

It is not so many years ago that leisure managers would hire their group fitness instructors just because they needed to fill a time-slot in the studio timetable; they would wade through a pile of CVs and simply call the first instructor who was qualified. Thankfully, this does not happen with such frequency any more: as managers started to recruit only after putting potential instructors through an audition process, they began to see the huge difference in standards between instructors with the same qualifications. The same goes for personal trainers and, in fact, it would be a good reflection upon your professional integrity to suggest that potential clients do go and speak to a few personal trainers so they can be sure of their choice.

Where should we meet?

The initial meeting could take place in the client's home. However, bear in mind here the safety aspects mentioned in Chapter 6. The advantages of meeting in the client's home are that the client will feel comfortable and you will also be able to assess the space they intend to use for exercise and any equipment needs. The disadvantages are the same as they would be when training clients at home, such as the need to minimise interruptions and to ensure you have the client's undivided attention. However, at least you will have the chance to see whether this would be an issue in the future.

Alternatively, if you work out of a gym or a studio, the meeting could take place there. This allows the client to check out the facility for themselves if they are not already a member and also saves you time as you don't have to travel to them. The only disadvantages here are that a gym setting can be intimidating for some people and it could give the client a slightly narrow vision of the work you could do together. The beauty of being a personal trainer is that you are not tied into working within four walls, so a client's connection and relationship with fitness can be radically altered as you design creative and fun ways to exercise outside of a gym environment. If you do meet in this setting, make sure there is somewhere private and comfortable where you can have the conversation and address all of the individual's questions.

As another alternative, the meeting could take place in a coffee bar or tearoom. Make sure you choose somewhere you know you can get a seat, where the music is not too loud and where you can get a relative amount of privacy. Hotel lounges often offer the perfect solution as they are frequently quieter, more intimate and can create a more professional and exclusive impression than a cafe.

What should I take?

Take your portfolio (qualifications, certificates, personal developments, achievements, testimonials and published articles, a starter pack, a couple of pens and your diary). The way you design your starter pack is obviously very personal, but it is good to give new clients something tangible when they decide to start training with you. It also ensures that new clients have all the information they need in one neat package. You could put all the paperwork in a well-designed folder that is in your company colours and incorporates your company logo. Your pack might include starter forms such as the PAR-Q, questionnaires, client agreement, terms and conditions, your profile, appropriate information sheets, client testimonials and so on. The list is endless, but for examples of client forms see Appendix 1.

How do I lead the conversation?

It is important that you take control at the meeting so that there are no awkward silences and so that the potential client leaves feeling taken care of. Remember that the client needs to feel that they have had all their questions answered and you need to feel comfortable that you know exactly what you are taking on should you decide to work together. Resist the temptation to sell hard as this will only lead to mistrust and discomfort for the prospective customer. The most important thing to do in this meeting is to ask the right questions and then shut up and listen. By all means take along a portfolio (see above) to prove your competence and let the person know that you are qualified, experienced and know what you are talking about, but conversation should be dominated by them rather than by you. Remember, given that you are qualified and perhaps knowledgeable in certain specialist areas, the most important factor in whether the person 'buys' from you will be how comfortable they feel with you. People buy from people. Your professionalism, enthusiasm and rapport-building skills (see pages 56–9) are actually far more important than the technical product at this stage!

What do I need to know?

Why does your prospective client want to hire a personal trainer?

What do they hope to achieve? Remember, the first answer they give you may not be the real answer at all. People may be slightly nervous and will say things they think you want to hear, or perhaps they don't really know what they want anyway. Probe their first answer, so when they tell you what they want, always ask, 'what else?' Keep asking until you feel you have got to the crux of what they want. A sample conversation might go something like this:

Trainer:	So, what do you want to achieve by working with a personal trainer?
Prospect:	I want to lose weight.
Trainer:	Good, what else?
Prospect:	I want to improve my strength.
Trainer:	OK. What other benefits do you think you can get from working with a personal trainer?
Prospect:	I really want to get into better shape.
Trainer:	Is there anything else?
Prospect:	No, not really. I don't know.
Trainer:	If you did know, what else might there be?
Prospect:	I don't know, my wife left me three years ago and I got very depressed, started drinking heavily and piled on the weight. I've given up alcohol altogether now, but I still can't shift the weight. Actually, what I really want is to have enough confidence in myself to get back into the dating game and get my life back on track.

At this point, reflect back the real reason to the prospective client and get a congruent acknowledgement. For example:

Trainer: OK. So, if you lose the weight, you will get more confidence, be able to start dating again and feel better about yourself. So, if we could put a programme together that could help you achieve that goal, how would that sound for you?

The reason you want to get to the real objective is that you will then be in a better position to decide whether you can offer what the prospective client needs and if you can, to motivate them in the longer term.

What is their exercise history and have they hired a personal trainer before?

It is useful to know what has stopped a person exercising in the past and also how many times they have tried to instil an exercise habit. Investigating what they have tried before will give you some clues as to what psychological approach to take. If the person has a history with another or several personal trainers in the past, it is good to know what their reason for leaving was – you don't want to be the next 'last trainer' six months down the line.

Taking the example above, the prospective client indicates that even though he has given up drinking alcohol, he is still finding it hard to lose weight. On closer investigation, the personal trainer discovers that this gentleman did join a gym at one point. He started really well, going six days a week and working really hard. However, he just couldn't keep it up and found he didn't really have the time, so he gave up. By the time he has the conversation with the personal trainer, he just feels too embarrassed about his size to do anything at all.

There are several clues here. The personal trainer now needs to use questioning to get to the root of the problem and discover why the prospective client stopped going to the gym. In this example, he worked too hard too quickly and did not get any proper guidance; in short, he burned himself out in his desperation to lose weight. He also discovered that six days a week was too big a sacrifice in his life and he simply did not have the time. By encouraging this client to start slowly, work towards realistic goals and fit an exercise routine into his lifestyle, the personal trainer can help him to avoid the pitfalls that befell him previously. Currently, the client has to get over several barriers in order to start exercising, but the fact that he is having the conversation at all is a good start and shows he might be ready to start a new exercise regime. Addressing the barriers would be a good place to begin. For example, if he feels self-conscious, working out at home might help. He has low confidence and has lost self-esteem, so setting short-term goals where he can see his progress quickly will start to instil some self-belief to carry him through the first few months and beyond.

What sort of exercise programme would they like?

They may not know the answer to this one if they are new to exercise, but asking what sort of activities they might like to try or have tried before and enjoyed will enable you to assess whether you have the skills to offer what they want. For example, let's say your prospective client is a keen golfer who wants to improve their game as well as their fitness. If you do not feel able to offer specific training in this area, then you should not take on this client.

Do they have any special needs or do they have any medical conditions?

Let's say the potential client suffered a recent heart attack and, having been through a phased cardiac rehabilitation system at their local hospital, now want to keep themselves as fit as they possibly can. If you are not qualified and competent in the area of cardiac rehabilitation, you should not even consider taking on the client. Be clear about your skills and knowledge, but also be very clear what you don't know. Referring the prospective client onto someone specialised in that particular area can only increase your reputation and your sense of personal integrity. If, in desperation to fill your practice, you take on clients whom you are either not qualified to teach or where you would be forced to practise outside your area of knowledge, then you are ripping your clients off and, at worst, could be in a vulnerable legal position should something go wrong.

The logistics

None of the above will be relevant if you are not free to train at the times your prospective client needs you. They will also need to know how much you charge.

The only reason to take on any new client is if it works for both you and the client. You will be working closely together and it is important to get the relationship off to a good start. Taking the time to get this right is invaluable.

Fitness assessment

A fitness assessment is any combination of formal and reproducible tests used to assess a client's ability to exercise or to give you baseline information about their current health status. During your first meeting with a prospective client, you may have learned something about their background, any goals they may have and a little about any medical conditions or health concerns they may have. However, you need to be very clear that this is no substitute for a thorough lifestyle evaluation and/or fitness assessment and you should not enter into any formal training programme without investigating further. You will only have superficial information thus far and will need to collect data and build on the rapport you have started to create. This will help you to really understand your client, their motivations and their needs so that you can work effectively with them.

You will have your own preferences and views about fitness and lifestyle assessment and you need to make your own decisions about just how much you do of each. In any case, you will need to arrange (separate from the first meeting discussed on pages 73–7) an appointment for this session prior to commencing training. Whatever you decide to do during the session, this is the point when you will go through any questionnaires, PAR-Q and goal setting.

We are very good at collecting data in the fitness industry: we think that by measuring everything we can then prove whether or not we have been successful. The problem is that sometimes we don't stop to think exactly why we do the things we do. This questioning is what sets the mediocre apart from the great trainers. There may be times when it is appropriate to do certain or even a barrage of traditional fitness assessments, but often this is not the case and fitness testing can be more of a hindrance and a barrier to participation than a help.

Below are some of the more familiar 'fitness tests' and advice on when it is best to use them.

Height and weight

Simple, quick and non-invasive, you may choose to measure the height and weight of any client with weight as an issue. This will enable you to measure their BMI (Body Mass Index), which is commonly used by the medical profession as a measure of over- or underweight (see page 114). It will also be necessary to take these measures if you want to measure a client's body fat percentage. However, if you do not need to measure body fat percentage and weight is not an issue for your client in any way, you probably would not choose to measure height and weight.

Blood pressure

You may wish to measure blood pressure for all your clients. It is quick and easy to carry out and is generally not threatening as most people will be used to this test from doctors and other health care practitioners. Taking a client's blood pressure could highlight a potential health issue and is good as a baseline figure for future health improvements. Remember that people with hypertension (see pages 118–20 for more information) may well not be aware of their health status and that exercising with uncontrolled hypertension is an absolute contraindication to exercise. Do be aware that you should never diagnose high blood pressure; this can only ever be done by a health professional and in any case would only be diagnosed if a high reading was recorded on three separate occasions. Also, remember that an individual's blood pressure reading may be high for several reasons: nerves, if they have just eaten a large or fatty meal or if they have drunk a caffeine-containing drink.

Body composition

Whichever way you choose to measure it, body composition is probably one of the most popular assessments. It can be useful for anyone who either wants to lose weight (body fat) or who is interested in the changes that will occur following training. Do consider, though, that it can be hugely demotivating if someone fails to lose body fat from one test to the next. In addition, if someone comes to you with a serious weight issue and they know they are overweight or obese, there may be little point in taking measurements to tell them what they already know. This could be threatening for some people, so always use your best judgement when offering assessments.

Anthropometric measurements

Girth measurements are again simple, non-invasive assessments that can be very motivating for any of your clients who want to lose or gain weight. Measures such as these, which are easy to understand and not technical, can demystify the whole fitness process and give clients a sense of mastery and control over their own health. Girth measurements are increasingly being used by the medical profession to identify health risks in terms of overweight and obesity.

Cardiovascular or VO_2

Whichever formal method of assessing you choose, you would need to have a good reason to carry out this test. Clients with whom you might carry out cardiovascular or VO_2 assessments include those who are particularly driven by assessment results or anyone who is training for a specific event or competition. However, for the majority of clients, its usefulness is questionable as you will be able to measure improvement by programme progression instead and VO_2 readings do not mean much to the majority of people anyway. Your clients will, however, understand if when they first come to you they cannot jog for more than two minutes at a time, but after a certain amount of time they are able to run for 30 minutes non-stop or even take part in a 10 km race.

If you have clients who are severely deconditioned, traditional tests for cardiovascular fitness may be inappropriate. Due to their physical condition, they may be unable to complete the test sufficiently to enable you to get a reading. In other words, they will not have the physical strength to finish the test and will give up before you get a VO_2 reading. In addition, you may come across clients who do not have the motor coordination necessary to undertake a test. For example, using a stationary bike or treadmill requires a certain amount of skill and there is little point in asking a client to carry out an assessment if they do not possess those skills. However, in such circumstances, and also for people suffering with medical conditions that have caused them to become seriously inactive, some form of cardiovascular assessment can be useful. In these cases, you could carry out simple (again comprehensible) assessments such as asking your client to walk between two points 10 metres apart, for example. Recording how far they can go in a minute can give you a really practical and easily reproducible assessment that is meaningful to your client.

Strength

There are many ways to measure strength. Grip strength has often been used as an indicator of overall strength. However, as strength is specific to the muscles being trained, this has little use for the general population. Simple sit-up tests might have a use if your client is particularly driven by assessments, but again, the results should only be used as a guide and not as an indication of overall strength. Programme progression will give you the best idea of how well your client is progressing and will give the best evidence of improvement. However, strength testing might be useful in competition as a way of benchmarking.

Flexibility

As with strength, flexibility tests only have relevance for the muscles being assessed and cannot be used as an indicator of overall flexibility. The most traditional test is that used for assessing the flexibility of the hamstrings. This may have its uses in specific cases: for example, you may have a client who is a keen footballer and has tight hamstrings from years of not stretching out properly. Here, assessment might help to make the point about the need for flexibility training and again could be used as a benchmark figure preceding a period of training that could include a strong focus on stretching.

Lung function

As with most other assessments, as peak flow measurements do not mean much in lay terms, lung function tests may be of limited use for the general population – unless, of course, you fully agree with the principle of fitness assessment and want to carry out the full barrage of tests as an extra service for your clients. However, in special populations, including anyone who has compromised lung function for whatever reason, assessing lung function might be a good method of showing improvements in lung capacity before embarking on a progressive cardiovascular programme. These populations might include clients with emphysema, anyone giving up smoking or someone who has previously suffered with pneumonia of any sort.

Postural evaluation

This probably has the most relevance for the majority of the population as it refers to body function in normal living. Thorough postural assessment is seen by some as being vital to the whole process of personal training.

The question is, why do you need this information? What purpose does it serve? If your intention is to show improvement and thereby prove your worthiness as a trainer and also to increase the motivation of your client, then fine. But what will give the best results? Often the simplest tests can be the most effective. Think about it – what do all the diet clubs and magazines do? They take before and after photos! So obvious, and yet only a handful of trainers actually do this. Similarly, girth measurements are the simplest and most effective measures of weight loss. People are often fascinated by body fat percentage; this might be a nice gimmick and, in some cases, fairly accurate, but certainly not essential. The average person has no idea what their body fat percentage should be, but they absolutely understand if they can buy clothes a size smaller!

Having said all this, there are of course benefits to assessment:

- Fitness assessments give you extra information about your clients. The various measures give you a snapshot of where your client is right now in terms of their fitness levels. Some trainers feel this helps them prescribe an effective exercise programme.
- For some personality types, the measurement of where they have come from and where they are now (by the next assessment) is a highly motivating tool. Be aware though that 'failure' or not accomplishing one's goals or seeing a change from one assessment to the next can be highly demotivating as well.
- Assessments can help you discover any medical, structural or postural needs that your clients may have. Sometimes in assessments you may detect medical problems that have not come to light elsewhere. Also, through postural assessment, you can create a programme that will bring your clients back into balance and enable them to function more efficiently.

You just need to be selective as to what you do and why.

Case study

David is 55 years old. He has not taken part in any formal exercise training for many years. He owns his own business, which has done very well. He enjoys the good life, but his work is very demanding so he sometimes suffers with stress. Over the past few years he has put on weight. His marriage has just broken down and he wants to make some changes to his lifestyle. On a recent visit to his GP, he was told he had high blood pressure and that he could do with losing weight and learning to relax a bit more. David has found this hard as he is very driven, although his blood pressure has now normalised following effective pharmaceutical intervention. His GP has suggested he take up exercise and has declared him fit to do so.

Given that David is 'driven', you might suppose he is quite goal orientated as well. Fitness assessment measures would therefore be quite appropriate for David. You would certainly take his blood pressure. He is finding it hard to lose weight, so girth measurements would also be useful: once he sees his waist circumference going down, he may be inspired to continue. He may well be someone who would enjoy having his body composition measured, which might help to educate him about the need to lose fat as opposed to weight per se. Finally, relaxation is an issue for David and it would therefore be worth exploring this area. Find out how he knows when he is stressed – what are the physical and psychological sensations he experiences and how do they affect his moods, habits and coping mechanisms? For example, does he eat more or drink more alcohol when he is stressed? This might help you to evaluate any changes experienced in his stress levels as a result of his exercise programme.

Case study

Katherine is 32 years old. She is a teacher. She loves her work and finds herself working long hours. She is fit and healthy, but has not exercised since leaving college nine years ago. Her mother has just been diagnosed with osteoporosis and, on reading about the condition, Katherine has become aware of her own health and the need to become more physically active. However, she does not really enjoy exercise and struggles to find time to do anything on her own. Joining a gym is something she really does not want to do. She has hired you to try to motivate her and to help her find some kind of physical activity that she will not only enjoy but that she can stick with.

Given Katherine's dislike of formal exercise training and gyms, fitness assessment might not fit so well with her. She does not have any specific fitness issues she wants to address, she just wants to look after her health in the long term and find some kind of activity she can enjoy. Other than the most basic assessments such as blood pressure, there is little point in doing much else. The main focus here should be on lifestyle assessment, goal setting and fun.

Goal setting

Goal setting is the one area in the lifestyle assessment that you would do with all your clients. While it is true that some people are more goal orientated than others, everyone can benefit from knowing what they want to achieve and working their way towards it. It is important that goals are constantly reassessed and reviewed to ensure they are current and achievable. There are occasions when we set goals for ourselves that either later become inappropriate because we have moved on in our plans and desires, or they become inappropriate because our circumstances have changed.

Much has been written about goal setting and, while it can be applied to all areas of our lives, it is crucial in the personal training business. Not only will effective goal setting motivate your clients, it will also enable them to see how successful they (and by association you) have been. In their extensive review of literature on goal setting, Locke et al. noted that goals serve as 'immediate regulators of human action' (Locke et al. 1981).

Goals vs wishes

It is first important to clarify with your client the difference between a goal and a wish. For example, a client may *wish* to lose weight, but unless they are prepared to take action it will remain a wish and they will never proceed any further. A *goal*, on the other hand, is a clearly defined result that is achievable through ongoing and measurable actions.

In setting their goal and establishing it as more than a simple wish, get your client to think as if they had already achieved the goal. When is the new weight achieved? They should put a date on it. Exactly how much weight have they lost? How does it feel to have achieved this? So, for example, the wish is to lose weight. The goal is: 'by 1 June, I will weigh 60 kilos. I will be able to walk down the aisle on my wedding day feeling confident and happy. I will have the wedding I've always dreamed of and will look exactly how I want to look.'

The SMART principle

The SMART principle of goal setting is a useful tool to enable your clients to understand the concept of goals vs wishes. Goals should be:

Specific – goals are always easier to visualise if you are very specific about the outcome: 'to get fit' is not specific; 'to complete a 10 km run' is.

Measurable – some goals are hard to measure.

For example, if a client wants to feel better and less stressed, it may be hard to define when they have achieved that goal. Digging a bit deeper, they might feel so tired at the end of a working day that they are only able to slump in front of the television. Therefore, one measure of improvement might be that they have the energy to go dancing twice a week after work. The example given above of the 10 km run is also measurable, of course.

Aspirational – the 'A' usually stands for 'achievable'. However, this can be very limiting because our concept of what is achievable is only based on our past successes. It is far more exciting and inspirational to set our goals at a level we may never have reached before. There is, of course, a balance to be made here so that your clients don't fail to achieve their goals, but it is great to aspire to be or do something. If Roger Bannister had stuck with achievable goals, he would never have run the four-minute mile because it was not considered possible at that time. Smaller 'achievable' goals along the way will allow your client to see progress.

Reward – again, there is a slight change from the norm here. 'R' often stands for 'realistic', which may fit well with 'aspirational' above. Aspirational is one thing, but the goal still needs to be realistic. So, your client may want to lose two stone in weight. This goal may be aspirational. However, it is not realistic to lose that weight in two weeks; that would be unhealthy and dangerous. 'Reward' is a good alternative or addition to 'realistic'. When goals are rewarded, your clients will be more likely to work hard to achieve them.

Time – putting a time scale on goals is vital. If you do not do this, the goal can become a wish that goes on for years. It is far easier to put a deadline on achievement as we tend to work harder over a set period of time.

However, remember that visualising the desired outcome and building confidence in your client's ability to achieve whatever they want to is more important than the SMART principle.

Therefore, the first step in helping your client to set goals is to determine exactly what it is they want to achieve. As we have seen, it is not enough to want to lose weight. They must decide how much and by when and ask themselves if they are prepared to do what it will take to get them to their desired objective. If we take losing weight as an example, your client may want to lose weight but also want to eat cake. In the simplest terms, it is not possible to do both, so the next step in getting them to really commit to the goal is to have them assess what achieving this will mean to them. A choice must be made and the client must see that the choice is theirs. They must take responsibility for their choices in life and therefore be in control when it comes to the pursuit of their goals. Goals should certainly be realistic, but the more challenging a goal is, the better a person tends to do. Work with your client to set goals that are demanding but attainable.

Commitment

Once your client has seen that achieving their goal is within their own power, you need to ascertain their level of commitment. In effect, if the person is not prepared to do what it takes, for example stop eating chocolate cake, the goal is not compelling enough. The cost of not eating chocolate cake is greater than the desire to lose weight. Many people beat themselves up constantly for not being able to achieve this kind of goal, when maybe they would be a lot happier if they just gave up on that goal. Helping your client get to the point at which they can make a good decision about this is a relatively simple process. Using the decisional balance system (see table 7.1), your client will be able to clearly weigh up the advantages and disadvantages of both change – in this case losing weight – and no change.

Table 7.1 Decisional balance system

	Advantages	*Disadvantages*
Change	• I would feel better about myself • I would be able to wear the clothes I want to • I would feel more attractive • I would be fitter • ... and so on.	• I would have to buy new clothes (could be an advantage!) • It would be hard work • I would have to give up sweets • ... and so on.
No Change	• I can eat chocolate cake • I feel comfortable • My friends like me as I am • ... and so on.	• I might die young • I can't play with my kids without getting puffed out • ... and so on.

'Throwing one's hat over the wall' is a good analogy here: once you have thrown your hat over, you have to find some way of scaling the wall after it! In other words, once a person has emotionally devoted themselves to something, they are capable of astonishing themselves and achieving things that they previously did not believe to be possible.

Support strategies

Encourage your client to talk about their goals with significant people in their life. This not only has the effect of rallying much-needed support, but will also create a situation where your client becomes accountable as people will ask how they are getting on and notice when things have not gone so well. When enlisting support, however, your client needs to realise that their nearest and dearest may not necessarily be their best source of support. It can be threatening for some people when a partner or close family member changes beyond what they currently recognise. It can make them feel deficient in their own ability to change, and if their friend/partner/etc. does change, it may threaten the very fabric of the relationship as they know it. Therefore, clients should be encouraged to share their goals, but be selective about who they share them with to maximise support and minimise any attempts at sabotage.

Write goals down

Goals should always be recorded in your client's file (see page 134 for a sample goals log), but also encourage your client to write the goal down themselves. The more detail they can put down and the more emotion they attach to it, the more likely the goal will be compelling and the client be unstoppable. They should write down exactly and specifically what the goal is, how it will be achieved and the date by which they will accomplish it.

Visual and written reminders

Encourage your client to keep visual reminders of their goal with them. They could stick a picture of how they will look once they have achieved their goal to the fridge door, or they could keep the written description of their goal with them in their diary. Another idea is to ask them to write something about their goal every day and keep that either in their diary or on a small card. Any simple cue that is creative and that works for your client should be encouraged. For example, your client could pick out pictures from magazines of clothes they would like to wear when they reach their goal, or there could be specific words they could use as motivators for change. These will of course be different for each person, but they should change the word often so it is always fresh in their mind and say it over and over like a mantra. Anything that helps to bring the desired goal into the everyday, as though it were already in existence, will help. This constant reminder will keep your client's mind focused and so encourage behaviours that are in alignment with the goal and its importance. Also, being reminded of their commitment when you are not around will stop your client from giving you the responsibility for success or failure. They need to learn that they are in control of their own lives – not you, their parents, their partner, their work, the government and so on. So, not only should they remember their goal every day, but they should take steps, however small, *every day* towards achieving it. Again, this helps to maintain interest, motivation and a sense of momentum.

Make a plan

Once the goals are clear, work with your client to make a workable plan to get them there. Making smaller goals along the way will allow your client to chart their progress and give them a sense of mastery over the situation. These goals or milestones should be things within your client's absolute control. For example, to lose two pounds in a week is not necessarily a goal one can control. However, to walk 15,000 steps per day or to cut out chocolate for a week are both completely within the client's power and are easily measurable.

Use positive affirmations

Encouraging your client to use positive affirmations related to their goal will enable them to focus on succeeding or winning whether you are with them or not. If they start to address their self-talk in this way, they will start to think of themselves as though they have already achieved the goal and their chances of success will be raised. For example, if their goal is to run a 10 km race by a certain date, they may say to themselves, 'I can run further and further each time I run'. They may also choose to think of their current habits differently so that they no longer associate themselves with the undesired habit. For example, if someone is addicted to sugar, they may say to themselves every time they are tempted to eat something sweet, 'I don't eat cakes' (or whatever).

Review goals regularly

Assist your client in sticking with long-term goals by constantly re-visiting them to confirm commitment or, if necessary, to re-negotiate and change the goals. Sometimes what was important at one stage can be a whole lot less important over time. If your client stays with outmoded goals, their interest will slacken and they can start to feel like a failure. This can affect their self-belief in other areas, so it is important to keep goals fresh and exciting.

Reward success

Finally, use reward and praise when your client has achieved even the smallest of sub-goals to keep the momentum going. If your client has enlisted the support of friends or partners in pursuit of their goals, then they should also reward small achievements to keep reinforcing success.

DESIGNING A TRAINING PROGRAMME

In this chapter you will:

- discover the issues involved in training clients in different environments
- uncover the programming principles that work.

General programming principles

The whole point of being a personal trainer is to design programmes that fit into an individual's lifestyle and help them to achieve their goals. This is the fundamental difference between you and a gym instructor. The 'one size fits all' approach will not work and you must use your technical knowledge and experience to design very specific workouts and strategies for your client. There are numerous books and courses on different types of training, from beginner to advanced, and this goes beyond the remit of this book. However, in this chapter we will cover basic principles of programme design and look at various different environments and modes of training.

In personalising your clients' exercise programmes, you will need to take the following into account:

- client goals
- referrer goals (if appropriate – see the section on medical referrals, pages 110–12)
- client's current fitness level
- any health or medical issues or limitations
- exercise history
- physical activity preference
- psychological factors such as motivation, confidence and so on
- time constraints
- available environment and equipment
- your scope of practice as a trainer.

You must adhere to the basic principles of programming. This will necessitate the client sometimes being outside their comfort zone. Overload must exist in order for there to be any training effect, and must be progressive and ongoing to continue to be effective.

Resistance training

Remember that for most clients resistance training should be designed to enable them to better cope with the demands of daily living. You need to be constantly thinking about the application of such exercises to your client's lifestyle: a good resistance training programme can assist in weight control by increasing metabolic rate, help conditioning for specific sports, correct posture, reduce the risk of injury and assist in activities of daily living.

Before progressing clients to the next level, ensure technique is perfected with slow and controlled movement at all times and that they have achieved adequate body awareness and co-ordination. Allowing for sufficient rest, overload should be no more than 10 per cent every 1–2 weeks. This will allow for the best form of conditioning. Ensure you produce a balanced programme (at least one exercise for each major muscle group) that addresses any specific problems arising out of daily misuse or sports. Always work large muscle groups first.

Clients should have at least 48 hours rest between strength training days to allow their muscles to recover. However, clients should not leave more than 72 hours between sessions or the gains will be lost.

Weight training systems

The systems described below are not really suitable for beginners. Depending on their ability, most clients would start with a simple whole-body programme consisting of single sets. This will allow your clients to familiarise themselves with movement patterns and equipment. It will also allow their bodies to become conditioned to training. From here you might devise a split routine, but still working with simple sets. As time goes on, they may wish to progress to other systems as detailed below. Obviously, with more advanced clients you can use these techniques from the start.

Pyramid training

This is a way of building muscle strength and size and involves altering weights over a number of sets. The muscle is warmed up by using lower weights and high reps to start with, then each set gets progressively heavier as the reps reduce. Aim for each set to take your client to near failure.

Pyramid systems are good for clients who want to increase their muscle size and strength. You would not use them for beginners, but would focus more on clients who have been weight training for over six months and want to move to the next level.

Supersets

The most common type of superset is when two opposing muscle groups are worked with no rest between sets, for example biceps followed by triceps. This can be a time-efficient method of training. Allow 2–3 minutes rest after supersets. This will help your client's stamina improve as it raises the anaerobic threshold. The second type of superset is very intense and involves two or more exercises on the same muscle group. This is excellent for producing hypertrophy, but be aware that it can lead to burnout and therefore should not be used at every session.

Again, this is a more advanced training system and should not be used with clients who are new to weight training.

Eccentric training

Your spotting technique needs to be excellent to offer your client confidence as they will be lifting greater than their 1RM (1 rep max) during this technique. You assist your client in lifting the weight through the concentric phase and allow them to *slowly* lower the weight themselves (eccentric phase). This technique should be reserved for advanced clients and only carried out after the body is thoroughly warmed up. It can be used after one or two sets have been completed to failure, but should only be used on one exercise per muscle group in each session. Be prepared to assist on the eccentric phase should you be needed. Prepare your client for greater muscle soreness following eccentric training and allow two weeks before training that muscle group again in this way.

Eccentric training is useful in that it promotes muscular growth more effectively than traditional training and enables clients to work to greater levels of intensity. However, due to the discomfort involved, this is another technique that should not be used with beginners – reserve it for more advanced clients.

Whichever system you use, or if you use no particular system, the number of sets needed for a successful weights programme is highly debatable. Generally speaking, if you are going for just one set, the intensity will need to be that much higher (though not with beginners). On the whole, multiple sets are better for the majority of people because the lower intensity will better encourage long-term adherence as it is more comfortable. Although performing multiple sets takes more time, it does have the added bonus of using more calories (if weight loss is the goal). Ideally, each set should be made up of 8–12 repetitions at 70–80 per cent 1RM. When you do increase the weight, you should do so by no more than 5 per cent at a time and obviously reps should be reduced accordingly.

Periodisation

Periodisation within a resistance training context refers to the cyclical change in the intensity of weights lifted with the total number of reps and sets. For example, one phase might be to lift low weights with high reps and the next might be heavy weights but low reps. The system is based on the principle that people cannot go on lifting more and more weight ad infinitum. Dr Hans Selye introduced the General Adaptation Syndrome theory (Kraemer, 1998), in which he describes three phases of adaptation when a person starts a resistance training programme. The first is the 'alarm' stage, which describes the stiffness and muscular discomfort individuals feel when they first start training. During the second phase, the individual gets stronger as the body adapts. The last stage is that of exhaustion, which occurs when the individual does not allow sufficient recovery or when they simply train too hard. Periodisation is a system whereby if you continually change the exercise regime, you avoid the final phase of the General Adaptation Syndrome.

Kraemer, Fleck and Evans (1996) suggested that this type of training ensures that each phase allows enough overload to produce a training effect to specific muscle fibres, while allowing adequate recovery in others. For example, when working in one phase, you will recruit more fast-twitch muscle fibres. In order to avoid burnout and exhaustion, when you change your routine you should target more slow-twitch fibres, thus allowing adequate recovery time.

Cardiovascular (CV) training

You should not be spending hours of time with your client while they do their CV training. That would be a waste of both their money and their time with you. However, you should be directing them to the types of CV training that will best help them achieve results. This should include specific instructions on mode, frequency, duration and intensity. Change your client's CV emphasis roughly every 2–4 months, which means working on a programme to improve their fitness over that short period with a specific type of CV training. This will include steady-state training (great for anyone with mental health issues as it creates a semi-meditative state that can take the focus off thinking too deeply) as well as interval training.

Many of your clients will be aware of the recommendation to achieve 30–60 minutes of moderate intensity physical activity on most days of the week. They may also know that this can be accumulated by splitting sessions up over the course of the day. For some of your clients, this may be a realistic goal, but for many you will need to refer to the ACSM fitness guidelines and progress your clients to 15–60 minutes of physical activity on 3–5 days per week at 60–90 per cent maximum heart rate.

The benefits of CV training include:

- reduction in cardiovascular risk factors
- improved blood lipids
- stress management
- reduced blood pressure
- assistance in weight control.

Cardiovascular programming

Choosing the appropriate method of training should always be done in conjunction with your client and, bearing in mind that they will be doing this on at least three days of the week and quite possibly without you at times, they need to find an activity that they enjoy or that is at least acceptable to them. Beginners, some older adults, obese and poorly conditioned clients should do low-intensity activity to encourage adherence and minimise discomfort. Walking is the obvious choice at this stage.

Steady state training

Steady state training will generally be for periods of 20 minutes or more (clients may need to build up to this) at low to moderate intensity, progressing by increases in duration. This type of training is good for clients wanting to lose weight and build up endurance and would be appropriate for beginners. It also offers cardiovascular risk factor management.

Interval training

Interval training, which is high-intensity work interspersed with low-intensity work, can build fitness quickly. It can be useful for beginners who cannot sustain aerobic activity over even a short period of time as well as for advanced clients who want to progress to the next level. With most clients you will do aerobic interval training, where the heart rate is elevated for periods of 2–15 minutes at a time with rest intervals lasting roughly the same amount of time. It may be appropriate for some advanced clients and athletes to use anaerobic interval training. This entails short bouts of very intense exercise with over 30-second intervals, for example sprint training. It will work muscles to fatigue. Circuit training is a variation of interval training and could incorporate resistance training as well if required. This could be used for a change to prevent boredom or as an alternative when a different location necessitates a change from the normal CV activity.

Fartlek

Fartlek (speed play) training is a type of interval training where intervals are not systematically measured, but depend upon how the participant feels on the day. Speed and gradient can be used to vary the pace.

Monitoring intensity

There are several methods to use when measuring the intensity of cardiovascular training.

Maximum heart rate (MHR)

In most cases, you will use age-predicted maximum heart rate as it is unlikely you will perform maximal capacity tests on your clients, except in special circumstances. To calculate maximal heart rate, subtract your client's age from 220 and the target training zone will then be a percentage of this figure.

For example, if your client is aged 35 years, their predicted maximal heart rate is 220 – 35 = 185 beats per minute (BPM). If they then want to work at 60 per cent MHR, they need to calculate 60 per cent of 185: 185 × 60% = 111 bpm. 90 per cent MHR would be: 185 × 90% = 166 bpm.

The main drawback to this system is its potential inaccuracy, as the figures can vary between individuals – two 35-year-olds with different fitness levels could have very different MHRs, for example.

Heart Rate Reserve (Karvonen Formula)

In this case, the resting heart rate is taken into account. To calculate, use the following formula:

(Maximal HR – resting HR) × desired intensity (50–85%) + resting HR

Thus, the same 35-year-old client with a resting pulse of 80 bpm wanting to work out at 70 per cent intensity would work this out as follows:

220 – 35 = 185 (MHR)
185 – 80 (resting heart rate) = 105 (heart rate reserve)
105 × 70% (intensity) = 73.5 (round this up to 74)
74 + 80 (resting heart rate) = 154 bpm

Borg's Rating of Perceived Exertion (RPE)

This measures intensity using a subjective view of feelings of exertion. You will see two scales in circulation. The first (see Table 8.1) uses the numbers 6–20 and this correlates well with heart rate response to exercise. Thus, if a client feels they are working at a rate of 14, their heart rate might be around 140 bpm. The modified version of RPE (see Table 8.2) uses a scale of 1–10, which is easier for clients to use.

Table 8.1 Rating of perceived exertion: 15-point category scale (Borg, 1973)

Number	*Perceived exertion*
6	
7	Very very light
8	
9	Very light
10	
11	Fairly light
12	
13	Somewhat hard
14	
15	Hard
16	
17	Very hard
18	
19	Very very hard
20	

Table 8.2 Rating of perceived exertion: 10-point category-ratio scale (Borg, 1982)

Number	*Perceived exertion*
0	Nothing at all
0.5	Very very weak (just noticeable)
1	Very weak
2	Weak
3	Moderate
4	Somewhat strong
5	Strong
6	
7	Very strong
8	
9	
10	Very very strong (almost maximal)

'Talk test'

If your client feels they are working hard, but can continue a conversation while working out, they are working to a safe and comfortable level. Again, this is a subjective measure, but can be useful in determining where your client feels comfortable when exercising and is a simple method for beginners to use.

The method you use to measure the intensity of cardiovascular training will vary from client to client. For example, newcomers to exercise may find the more subjective methods such as RPE or the 'talk test' easier to use, whereas more advanced clients may prefer to use the formulas on pages 88–9.

Flexibility

Stretching is often underemphasised in fitness training and part of your job is to educate your client in its importance as part of a well-rounded programme. There is controversy over the usefulness of stretching, but it is thought that it can help prevent injury and maintain range of motion as well as aiding relaxation and making everyday tasks easier. In any case, it is widely accepted that flexibility is an important part of any fitness programme.

The following points should always be followed:

- Never force a stretch. Stop at the point of mild tension or resistance.
- Stretch in a slow and controlled manner.
- Warm muscles respond much better to stretching, so the best time to perform stretches is at the end of a workout.

- Ensure the stretches are specific to the workout; you need to stretch the muscles your client has used in the workout.
- If you are assisting your client in a stretch, make sure you listen to their feedback constantly.
- Ensure your client is not holding their breath. This is a common problem and clients should be encouraged to breathe normally throughout the stretch.
- As in other components of training, flexibility will only increase with overload. Slow and sustained stretches are the safest way to achieve this.
- Hold stretches for a minimum of 20 seconds, and preferably 30–60 seconds.
- Remember that age, inactivity and even gender have an effect on flexibility. Always work with the individual as to what feels comfortable.
- Take account of medical conditions during stretching as well as during other components of the session. Recent injury, joint inflammation and osteoporosis are all things to be wary of and any severe pain during stretching is a definite warning sign. In these cases, it is best to get advice from a clinician or doctor before proceeding.

Overtraining

Be aware of the symptoms of overtraining. These may include irritability, depressed immune system, increased susceptibility to injury and muscle soreness, lack of motivation to exercise, depression, fatigue and insomnia. If there is a possibility that your client is overtraining, ensure they take a break from their regime and eat a carbohydrate-rich diet.

Where to train

You will also need to decide where to train with your clients. The three main options are in a gym, at the client's home or outside. Over the next few pages we will look at some of the considerations you will need to take into account in each training environment.

Training in a gym

See Table 8.3 for the advantages and disadvantages of training in a gym.

Training at your client's home

See Table 8.4 for the advantages and disadvantages of training at your client's home.

Equipment

When training someone in their own home, you are obviously limited by lack of equipment. However, this also allows you to be far more creative in your work. If you are training many clients at home, there is clearly a lot you can do simply using the client's own body weight. However, it may be appropriate for you to purchase your own equipment and, in some cases, your clients may well wish to buy their own.

Below is a list of equipment you may want to consider. However, it is by no means exhaustive and new and interesting items come onto the market all the time.

- step for warm up/CV work; can also be used for strength work
- dumbbells
- bands/tubing – these are a great piece of equipment for many clients as they are cheap and take up no room at all; once confident in their use, you could even design programmes for your client to take away with them when they travel, which is particularly useful for those who travel by necessity on business
- exercise ball
- medicine ball – excellent for sport-specific

training and also to assist in abdominal and power work
- skipping rope
- boxing gloves and pads
- wobble board.

Some clients may have the money and room to purchase larger pieces of home-exercise equipment such as a treadmill, stepper, elliptical trainer, rower or even a small multi-gym. It can be a good idea for you to help them choose equipment (see Chapter 3 as you may want to add this to your list of useful people/contacts). Make sure they pay you for your time in doing this, or perhaps use one or two sessions to go with them and help them choose. There is a huge range of quality in-home exercise equipment and it can be costly, so the correct choice is vital. If the new kit breaks down during early usage, this can lead to clients becoming disheartened and possibly losing interest in their training programme.

Training outside

See Table 8.5 for the advantages and disadvantages of training outside.

Walking/jogging/running

Walking is great for any client who is limited in the intensity of their training, although hill walking can prove challenging for even advanced exercisers! Any client with a very low fitness level, some older clients or clients with specific medical conditions or injuries will benefit from fitness walking. The beauty of this mode of exercise is that clients can easily replicate this activity on their own. So long as you train them in correct technique, how to measure their intensity and ideas for routes, they are perfectly able to be set targets between sessions.

Clients may wish to progress to interval training or fartlek training (see page 88).

Cross-training

Cross-training is a good way of adding variety for clients who you train outside. By combining several different types of exercise, you can effectively build a good cross-training workout, varying the mode, intensity and duration for different levels of ability. This is a good way of building endurance without overtraining particular muscle groups and can help to increase calorie usage as the body does not get used to just one mode of training. Table 8.6 shows a simple cross-training programme for a client who wants to lose weight and generally get fitter.

Stretching and strength training

Some parks have terrific fitness circuits already built in. However, you can also use the natural environment in loads of creative ways. Park benches work well for dips and stretching, trees are good to lean against for standing press-ups and for ski squats, kerbs (not on a busy road!) are good for step-ups and hills are great for higher intensity training or to train different muscle groups.

Safety

Remember that your client's safety is your number one priority at all times. When taking your client into different environments, you will need to take safety precautions such as:
- Take a first-aid kit with you in case of any emergencies.
- If your client is asthmatic, ensure they take their inhaler.
- Ensure your client is appropriately dressed for the weather and remember to take sunscreen if the sun is out.
- Take water with you.
- Take your mobile phone with you.

Other modes of training and having fun

It is vital to keep your clients' training programmes fresh, and suggesting they try other activities from time to time or even to balance the programme you offer can be highly beneficial. If you happen to teach yoga, Pilates, tai chi or martial arts, then great, but obviously never teach any disciplines you are not qualified in. Every now and then, inject some fun and frivolity into the everyday routine. I know one trainer who takes his clients to the local leisure pool every so often. Climbing the stairs to the flume, scooting down and swimming to the edge may sound like child's play, but by the 20th time it can prove to be a demanding workout. Playing like children occasionally can take the edge off what can sometimes seem like a very serious discipline.

Alternatively, just changing location can inject something new into a workout. If you always train within a gym or at home, get outside on a nice day. Park playgrounds have bars and poles that, when combined with exercise tubing, make resistance work that bit different. Other options include biking, rollerblading, swimming or tennis. But always make sure you only teach what you are qualified and competent to teach.

Table 8.3 Advantages and disadvantages of training in a gym

Advantages	*Disadvantages*
1. Programming is relatively easy as there is lots of good equipment to choose from to keep clients interested and you can change programmes frequently. 2. Some clients may find it easier to train in a gym setting, as making themselves go to the gym can motivate them. 3. As a trainer you have support should things go wrong or an injury occur.	1. You are limited to clients who are members of that gym. 2. You may find it limiting to train your clients during peak times when the gym is crowded and access to equipment is more stretched. 3. Some clients may be intimidated by a gym environment. 4. Training in a 'normal setting' that is closer to activities of daily living can make it easier for some clients to train without you in between sessions. 5. If you work within a gym, you will probably have to pay for the privilege either by giving the gym a percentage of your takings, by paying a monthly fee or even having to be employed by the gym in order to work there.

Table 8.4	**Advantages and disadvantages of training at your client's home**
Advantages	*Disadvantages*
1. Clients feel most comfortable at home. They do not have to worry about what to wear and do not feel self-conscious. One of the greatest barriers to exercise for most people is that they feel nervous about going into a gym environment where they perceive everyone to be fitter, younger, more good looking, more trendy (the list goes on!) than they are. For many people, they simply do not see themselves as the sort of people who could or would want to use a gym. 2. Clients do not have to pay for a gym membership on top of your personal training fees. 3. The client's time commitment is minimised. Another big barrier to people committing to an exercise programme is lack of time. 4. Clients learn how to exercise within their own home and with minimal equipment. If they are not dependent on a gym for their programme, they are more likely to do what is needed between sessions with you. 5. Clients will feel a greater sense of commitment when you are visiting them.	1. You must factor travel time into your scheduling and pricing. The more time you spend travelling, the fewer clients you can fit in. 2. Clients may feel too comfortable at home and clear boundaries must be set: a. Sessions will start and finish on time regardless of whether the client is ready at the appointed start time. b. All distractions must be minimised, which means all phones and televisions turned off and children must be in someone else's care for the duration of the session.

Table 8.5	**Advantages and disadvantages of training outside**
Advantages	*Disadvantages*
1. For many clients who live in inner cities and/or who have stressful jobs, training outside can have therapeutic benefits in addition to the exercise. 2. Training outside can allow for increased variety and can increase the sense of fun as new activities are experienced.	1. Be aware that some clients may feel self-conscious outside. 2. You cannot rely on the great British weather! You may plan the greatest outdoor session and have to change your plans at the last minute, so you will always need a back-up plan.

Table 8.6 Sample cross-training programme

Day	*Activity*	*Duration*
Monday	Brisk walking with some hill work Stretching Lower-body weight training	20–30 minutes 5–10 minutes 30 minutes
Tuesday	Jogging at a steady pace Stretching Upper-body weight training	20–30 minutes 5–10 minutes 30 minutes
Wednesday	Yoga	60 minutes
Thursday	Spinning class Stretching	45 minutes 5–10 minutes
Friday	Brisk walking Total-body weight training	20 minutes 20–30 minutes
Saturday	Jogging at a varied pace Stretching	30–45 minutes 5 10 minutes
Sunday	Rest	

CLIENT GROUPS

9

In this chapter you will:

- discover the major points to look out for with different types of client, from athletes to the obese
- discover how to create links with the medical profession to tap into referred populations.

There is of course no typical client, and most people will have some kind of physical or psychological issue to deal with. This chapter is designed to give you the basic information you need to work with some of the more common low-risk population groups. Bear in mind, however, that while this chapter gives an overview and can be a useful reminder, you will still need to acquire the necessary evidence that you can work with specific client groups and, once you get into some of the more 'risky' medical conditions, you will need to attend a training course and become qualified. This might include a GP Referral qualification or condition-specific courses such as Cardiac Rehabilitation or HIV.

In each section, I have made suggestions of courses you could take to learn more about that client group. Most of these are short courses that will give you Continuing Professional Development points (required for maintenance on REPs). As with all courses and qualifications, there is huge variation both in the standard of teaching but also in the depth of knowledge presented. So, for example, you may be able to cover a subject in a one-day course or a four-day course – you will therefore need to make your own decision as to what your requirements are.

Clearly, if you plan to specialise in one area, you will want as much knowledge as possible. If, on the other hand, you just have one client with a specific need, you may choose to go for the bare minimum to ensure you can deal safely and effectively with the situation. If you are a member of REPs, you must ensure that the course you want to do is endorsed by them so that you can use the points to keep your membership updated.

A full client history should always be taken and, as most people have a complex set of issues and/or conditions, the exercise prescription must always be carefully tailored to suit the individual and not the condition. Where health professionals have given advice, you should always take this into account and, if in any doubt whatsoever, seek medical guidance.

Referring on and knowing your own scope of expertise

There will be times when a new or existing client presents with conditions that you cannot cope with. This may be for a number of reasons, such as a medical condition that falls outside your scope of expertise or psychological problems that lead you to believe that this person might endanger themselves or you. It is vitally important you are honest with yourself and don't let your desire for a full client list blind your sense of reason. At these times it is useful to have a tactful and professional way of dealing with the client and also, where appropriate, a list of professionals who you may be able to refer on to.

Pregnancy – ante-natal

Overview/must know

Historically, there has been a lot of concern over pregnant women engaging in a physical activity programme. However, it has now been widely accepted that normally pregnant, healthy women can benefit from continuing or starting an exercise regime. Indeed, it can offer improved fitness and posture, help improve stamina and thus help with delivery, hasten post-birth recovery, limit weight gain and offer improved psychological benefits.

During the first trimester the foetus goes through an important growth phase and the expectant mother may feel tired sooner in response to changes in the body. She must be careful to balance exercise, rest, hydration and nutrition. Over the rest of the pregnancy, she will typically gain 10–16 kg.

Other changes in the body during pregnancy include an alteration in the way food is metabolised, such that fat is more likely to be stored (predominantly around the breasts, thighs and bottom) and not used. The ligaments will be far more elastic due to the increase in relaxin. This allows the pelvis to expand and the joints to become more mobile.

Exercise considerations

The first trimester can leave many women feeling very unwell and for this reason they may not wish to take part in their regular physical activity or they may feel they need to modify their programme. In this case, gentle yoga, Pilates and swimming are all viable alternatives. Some women will be fine to continue as normal, although strenuous physical activity should be avoided at this time.

Clients should avoid excessive heat and over-heating while exercising. However, a fit and healthy pregnant woman will be more efficient at controlling her body temperature than a pregnant but sedentary woman.

During later pregnancy, as the woman's centre of gravity changes, balance and agility exercise will prove difficult. Women may be more clumsy and unable to move quickly at this time. Due to the excess weight at the front of the body, women may experience lower back pain and this is where exercise in water can be very helpful.

The production of relaxin during pregnancy serves to make joints more mobile, but also means that care should be taken to avoid taking joints beyond the normal range of movement and thereby decreasing joint stability. To this end, be aware when stretching and only take the stretch to a joint's normal range. In addition, avoid fast or jerky movements, which might result in hyperextension of the joint.

Exercise recommendations

Guidelines for exercising during (uncomplicated) pregnancy are very similar to those for the general population, in that women should accumulate 30 minutes of moderate intensity exercise on most days of the week. Other recommendations include:

- Ensure you screen carefully for any contraindications to exercise and continue to ask questions on a regular basis to check that none have occurred in the meantime.
- Avoid any exercise or activity that could cause injury to the abdominal area.
- Do not ask your client to do any activity or relaxation in the supine position after the first trimester. This position may cause your client to feel faint.
- Exercise programmes should be adapted to take into account balance and co-ordination issues.
- Ensure your client is consuming enough

calories to take exercise into account. An active woman will need over 3000 calories per day in later pregnancy.
- Consider both weight-bearing and non-weight-bearing activity for your client. Always be guided by what she feels most comfortable with. There is some opinion that you should focus more on non-weight-bearing activity and in this instance swimming and stationary cycling are both great options that will really help your client to stay fit and well.
- Walking, light jogging and low-impact aerobics are all appropriate activities as long as your client is comfortable.
- Exercise intensity should not be greater than pre-pregnancy levels.
- Previously inactive women should start off gently and increase their activity levels only gradually. Similarly, if a previously active woman needs to limit her activity during the first trimester, but then wishes to start again, she should do so only gradually.
- Resting every so often may help to avoid foetal hypoxia (where blood flow is diverted away from the foetus and towards the mother's muscles during exercise) and also thermal stress due to a rise in the mother's core temperature.
- Avoid developmental stretching during pregnancy due to the presence of relaxin, which makes ligaments much more flexible than normal.
- During the third trimester, it is vital that your client listens to her own body, although she can continue to be physically active for as long as she is comfortable to do so. Hydration and temperature are both really important issues at this point.
- Postural work, pelvic floor and core stability (not curl-ups!) are all suitable during the third trimester and may be done kneeling on all fours (if carpal tunnel syndrome is not present). Relaxation (not lying supine), breathing exercises, lower back extensions and trapezius work are also ideal.
- It is vital that you know the reasons to discontinue exercise. The following would all indicate that your client should stop exercising immediately and seek medical help: abnormal pregnancy progression, vaginal bleeding, membrane rupture, persistent pain, dizziness, palpitations or chronic fatigue.

Avoid the following during pregnancy:

- scuba diving
- any activity that takes you to high altitude (over 1800 metres)
- contact sports or any activity that poses a risk of abdominal injury
- cycling (not including stationary) because of balance issues in later pregnancy
- any activity that would make your client strain, such as heavy weightlifting
- highly competitive activities.

Contraindications to ante-natal exercise

Pregnant women with any of the following should not take part in an exercise programme:

- heart disease
- constrictive lung disease
- pregnancy-induced hypertension
- pre-term labour with previous pregnancies
- intra-uterine growth retardation
- incompetent cervix
- placenta previa
- premature rupture of membranes.

Qualifications

Many of the major training providers (see pages 143–4 for contact details) include ante- and post-natal exercise courses in their portfolio. These are between one and three days long, depending on your provider.

Marketing

As this is such a niche market, you will come across it in one of two ways: you will either have an existing client who becomes pregnant, or you may target this area as a specialism within your personal training practice. If you are specialising in this area, much of your business will come through word of mouth as parents tend to know each other through antenatal clinics, schools and kids' clubs. With this in mind, you could offer incentives to current clients who introduce a friend and similar promotions. Don't forget to ask clients for referrals. Many people miss out simply because they don't ask!

Other places to advertise for this client group would be in ante- and post-natal clinics themselves. A poster on the clinic wall may suffice, but think about producing leaflets as well. If you are a group fitness instructor as well as a personal trainer, you could run a class, which could also generate more personal training clients.

Pregnancy – post-natal

Exercise recommendations

Clients returning to exercise after the birth of their child should be carefully screened. There should be no vaginal bleeding, other than normal menstruation, blood pressure should have returned to normal and the uterus should have returned to its normal size and position (a post-natal examination carried out by their doctor will confirm this to be the case).

Emphasis should be placed on re-training postural alignment and on correct technique during all physical activity. It will be helpful to focus on common movements such as feeding and lifting a baby in relation to back care.

The effects of relaxin can still be present for up to five months post-partum. Therefore, there may only be a need for maintenance stretching during this period and you should be aware that joint stability will still be vulnerable. Developmental stretching should not restart until at least 16–20 weeks post-delivery.

Avoid high-impact exercise for several months to enable the joints to become more stable and for the pelvic floor to recover sufficiently. Focus instead on low-impact activity, directing your client towards correct joint alignment at all times. Also advise your client to wear a strongly supportive sports bra.

Clients can return to resistance training if they were lifting during their pregnancy. If they did not do any resistance training during pregnancy, they can lift 70 per cent of their pre-pregnancy weight. If you have a client who is new to resistance training, you should focus on core conditioning before starting a resistance training programme.

Abdominal work is obviously crucial to a post-natal conditioning programme. Gentle, hospital-recommended abdominal work can begin within 24 hours post-delivery. During pregnancy, the rectus abdominis will have stretched and separated. This can take six weeks or more to heal. Although you will not resume formal training with your client at this stage, advise them to avoid abdominal work kneeling on all fours until at least six weeks after giving birth. Take extreme care when exercising the abdominals.

As the pelvic floor will have been severely affected during pregnancy, it is essential to start exercises for this area as soon as possible after delivery. Many women will be concerned about starting too soon, but it will actually aid recovery if they start early.

Always start gently and increase slowly with post-natal exercise. Failure to do so could delay the healing process. Wait at least six weeks after delivery to begin exercising (8–10 weeks for caesarean deliveries) and certainly until after a post-natal check-up indicates that it is safe to do so.

Stress management

Many clients will come to you because they are stressed and would like to use exercise to assist them in managing their stress levels. Even if this is not their primary reason for approaching you, you will find a lot of your clients want to manage their stress anyway. Physical activity can be a good antidote to stress for most people and you will be ideally placed to assist clients further if this is an area you and your client choose to focus on. In addition, even if your client does not specifically want to work on stress, you may find that the level of stress in their lives and the unhelpful ways they deal with that stress impacts on their training. You may find that their unhelpful coping mechanisms sabotage their efforts to be physically active and to eat well. As with all the sections in this chapter, whole books have been written about this subject and this really is a starting point, but hopefully it will give you some useful tools with which to begin.

What is stress?

There are many definitions of stress, but perhaps the most widely accepted is by Richard Lazarus who said, 'stress arises when individuals perceive that they cannot adequately cope with the demands being made on them or with threats to their well-being' (Lazarus, 1966). It is important to note here the idea of perception: people cope with demands in different ways and what might be perceived as being stressful to one person is no problem to another. So, whether a demand turns into something the individual feels they cannot cope with is a very personal thing. When that happens, however, the demand becomes a 'stressor'.

Responses to stress

There is good and bad stress. Good stress is short-lived and allows us to achieve things we might not otherwise have done or to have enormous fun. Examples include the stress you feel when you have to give a presentation or performance, the thrill you feel when you go on a scary funfair ride or the stress you need to respond quickly in a dangerous situation. Bad stress occurs when we live in a constant state of tension. When the body encounters a perceived threat or stressor, it reacts in several ways: increased heart rate, increased sugar and fat levels in the blood and inhibited digestive secretions, among many other reactions. This is known as the 'fight or flight' response. This response is a basic human function designed to protect us in times of great need, such as when we are at risk of being killed. In this instance, the physiological response enables fast reaction to the danger and an enhanced ability to fight or get away. It is a useful and necessary reaction in certain situations, such as when we are truly under threat. The problem arises when we live in a constant state of arousal and threat. Keeping the body in this mode for extended periods leads to ill health and disease. In particular, high levels of stress can lead to (or be a causal factor in) many conditions and diseases, such as angina, anxiety, drug and alcohol misuse, depression, heart disease, hypertension, stroke, ulcers, fatigue and headaches to name a few. Stress also impacts on our mental health as well as our relationships and our work.

How does exercise help?

Exercise in itself is good for any clients who suffer with stress. It helps the individual to 'switch off' and temporarily not think about whatever is the source of their stress. This ability to get out of their mental turmoil and to engage with their physical body is immensely powerful, allowing them to return with a more refreshed attitude. In addition, the physical responses to exercise all aid in promoting a more relaxed response to life. However, the psychological side of this cannot be ignored. As we saw earlier, it is the *perception* of our experiences that causes us to feel stress or not and it is within our power to control our response.

Step-by-step approach to stress management

The first step in helping clients with stress management issues is to help them identify their stressors. Have them make a list of the things in their life that cause them to experience stress. This can be split into those that are directly in their control and those that aren't.

Next, identify the cues that lead your client to know that they are stressed. In effect these are the symptoms and may include craving sweet or 'junk' foods, irritability, a constant butterfly feeling in the stomach or a feeling of panic. Everyone's response is different. The issue here is to raise your client's awareness when they experience stress so that they are better placed to do something about it.

You can now eliminate or decrease stressors where possible. You could go through your client's list of stressors and ask your client for ideas of how to do this. For example, if they feel stressed because they are overwhelmed at work with too much to do, your questioning technique should lead them to find their own solution to the stressor. Perhaps they need to learn to say 'no' more or to negotiate with their boss rather than trying to be over-helpful all the time. Perhaps they could delegate more or maybe they need to learn not to be such a perfectionist. Only they will know the answer.

You also need to identify current coping mechanisms. This may not always be that obvious, as some of our coping methods are unconscious. However, we are creatures of habit and your client will continually resort to the same methods. Some will be helpful, others unhelpful or destructive, such as drinking too much alcohol or eating too much, too little or badly – many people use food as a coping method as we try to self-medicate with our diet. Good coping mechanisms would be attending a yoga class or daily meditation or perhaps just taking time out to do something for themselves. You need to check, though, that these are not just avoidance games that ultimately make you feel more stressed.

Finally, plan an alternative response. Work with your client to identify when stressful periods may be coming up and to prepare thoughtfully so that they are better able to cope with positive responses. On occasion, it may be appropriate to do some relaxation within the session, encouraging them and giving them ideas about how they could do this alone.

Relaxation techniques

It may be useful to teach your client some simple relaxation techniques, discuss what they are consciously doing to relax and possibly even spend time at the end of their sessions on relaxation if they need it. There are very many relaxation and meditation techniques available and the regular practice of these will not only enable your client to elicit that feeling of relaxation during times of tension, but they will also feel more relaxed in general.

In carrying out any relaxation techniques, guide your client towards the following recommendations:

- eliminate as many distractions as possible
- make sure you will not be interrupted and that the temperature is comfortable

- take off your shoes and loosen any tight clothing
- sit or lie in a comfortable position and dim the lights – natural light is best
- you may also find it helps to put on some soothing music – there is specific relaxation music available, or many people find that some classical music can be very therapeutic.

The techniques listed below provide a variety of quick, easy and instant relaxers as well as some that will take a little longer. If you do take your client into a deeply relaxed state, bring them out of it slowly and gently. They should sit still for a few moments afterward and allow time to 'come to'.

Progressive Muscle Relaxation

This is good for people who need something concrete to focus on. It involves progressively relaxing the muscles of the body one by one, working up from the toes to the head. At each stage tell yourself to relax and feel the muscle becoming heavy, warm, relaxed, etc. Focus on breathing deeply and slowly throughout.

Meditation

Sit quietly, close your eyes and focus on your breath for a few seconds. Now, on every 'out' breath, say a word silently to yourself. This word could be 'one' or 'relax', or you may choose to say 'let' on the 'in' breath and 'go' on every 'out' breath. Every time you feel your thoughts wandering, just keep returning to the word or words. Stop after a while and just sit with your eyes closed for a short time, then with your eyes open, before moving. Build up the time spent on this as it will get easier. You might only start with one minute, but it will still make a difference.

Visualisation

Use visualisation techniques to promote deep relaxation. Again, sit or lie comfortably, close your eyes, take a deep breath and relax. Talk your client through this or they can do this alone, but imagine a scene such as a beautiful beach on a warm summer day. As you talk through the scene, tap into the different sensations of sight and colour, the warmth of the sun, the smell in the air and the sound of the ocean.

In addition to these techniques, make your client aware of other simple rituals and habits they can create for themselves that will help them feel more relaxed. For example, encourage the use of aromatherapy oils in the home, office or car and some people find flower remedies and essences helpful. These are available from health food shops. Your clients should also be encouraged to make time for themselves on a regular basis to read, listen to music or do some other activity they find relaxing.

When to contact a doctor or refer on

Always remember that you are a personal trainer and your job is primarily about training your client in physical activity. However, stress is such a huge problem that clients may find that their stress levels sabotage their attempts at lifestyle change. This is where you can use your skills and the tools listed above to assist. Just be aware that there may be times when you feel that your client is in need of more intensive help to address personal issues. If this is the case, do refer them on to a trained therapist.

Qualifications

No formal training is required to work with this client group, which is probably just as well because most of your clients will suffer with stress at some point! There are, however, a number of short courses on stress. Contact any of the fitness training providers (see pages

143–4 for details) to see if they run one near you. Sometimes this area is covered in other courses such as client lifestyle and appraisal.

Sport-specific training

You may well have clients who are training for and who compete in a specific sport. If so, you will clearly need to adapt your training programme to the specific requirements, both physical and mental, that this entails.

Exercise considerations

When training a client for any sport, it is important to always remember the whole person. An athlete's coach will know about all aspects of their client's life because the level of stress they feel in all areas (including home, finances and relationships) will affect their performance. As a personal trainer, your own level of involvement will depend on the level of involvement your client has in their chosen sport. If they are at elite level, you will need to pay attention to their whole lifestyle including what they do when they are not with you (for example distracting relationships, alcohol or excessive caffeine consumption); if they are at a lower level, you will not need to be as involved.

While specificity is clearly one of the most crucial laws of training for a sport, remember that cross training may have its uses as well in terms of overall athleticism and increasing the athlete's ability to recruit different muscle fibres for different needs.

Periodisation

Periodisation is a way of planning the training year around the sports person's needs to enable them to be in top form when the competition season approaches and even to peak at a specific competition. This is one of the most important principles in training competitive athletes and has been around since 1965 when Matvayev updated earlier work in this area. In his system, the year is divided into three main parts: preparation, competition and transition (Matvayev, 1966). These parts are several months long and are known as macrocycles. Each macrocycle is then subdivided into smaller portions of time known as mesocycles (2–6 weeks in length) and microcycles (one week).

The **preparation** phase is the longest of the three cycles and will last for up to four months. During this time, the athlete should increase their volume of training for the whole body, using the major muscle groups and cross training. Some specific skills training will be involved.

The **competition** macrocyle will begin 2–3 months before the season begins. Intensity and specificity will both be ramped up and the athlete will focus on technique. Pre-competition, the main focus is on skill building and psychological preparation, although general training may be used as active rest. Training will be high intensity but low volume. The athlete may take part in small competitions before taking a short break. The main competition period may last for 2–6 weeks. In sports that have a longer season such as football, hockey and rugby, players can be expected to play at full pelt for far longer. At elite status, players will be rotated to allow for adequate rest; however, if your client is not at that level and demands are being made on their performance, it will have a negative effect on their stress levels and ability to perform. Making your client aware of this so that they don't expect their top performance at every game of the season will help. Instead, it would be prudent to focus on the most important games. The athlete must have adequate rest during this time, with low-volume but high-intensity training.

Finally, the **transition** phase allows the athlete to rest and recover before starting the cycle again. This is a vital part of the process and it is important the athlete does some activity, but this should be far more general with the emphasis on rest and relaxation. The period might last for 3–6 weeks following a hard competition phase.

Qualifications

There is a clear difference between personal training a client who plays a certain sport and coaching at elite level. As a personal trainer, you may choose to do either or both of these. You may find it useful to have specific sports coaching qualifications in addition to your personal training ones: Many of the major training providers offer the Sports Conditioning Course, which would be the one to go for if you are interested in this area, or contact Sports Coach UK for more information (see page 144 for details). This will give you more of a focus on sport as opposed to fitness and will allow you to concentrate on a very specific area. With both sets of qualifications at your disposal, you will be in a good position to train any athlete (elite or amateur). Of course, whatever sport your client is focused on, you will need to understand the game and its particular demands on the body.

The complete beginner

The challenge when working with complete beginners is to work to a level at which they feel comfortable and never to patronise. PT's tend to work inside a 'fitness bubble', but if your client is completely new to exercise you will need to be able to empathise with their current position and adapt your programmes accordingly. Never be shocked at just how little some people can do: if someone is severely deconditioned, even the most moderate of programmes could prove challenging. The need to individualise the programme is never truer than with complete beginners.

Exercise considerations

In order to give you a general overview of working with complete beginners, in this section we have presumed that your complete beginner client is an apparently healthy adult. However, in real life you should never assume this to be the case and you should always carry out a lifestyle and/or fitness assessment with any new client. This would include the PAR-Q and questioning from you to discover if there is any reason your client should not be physically active.

Exercise recommendations

Beginners will not need to work to a high volume or intensity as they will make fast improvements at this stage. For example, in the first 6–8 weeks, they need do one or two sets only in their resistance training.

ACSM recommendations for the progression of cardiovascular exercise suggest three distinct phases: initial conditioning, improvement conditioning and maintenance. The **initial conditioning phase** should last for 4–6 weeks. Clients should begin by doing 12–15 minutes of activity every other day and increase gradually. This will depend upon functional capacity at the start. Clients should not progress to the next level until they can comfortably complete 30–40 minutes of activity on five days of the week.

The **improvement conditioning phase** will last for 4–5 months. During this time, intensity will gradually increase to 60–90 per cent of maximum heart rate and will eventually be sustainable for at least 20 minutes. Obviously, your client's fitness level and response will determine duration and actual intensity used at the beginning.

The **maintenance phase** kicks in when your client has achieved their goals or target functional capacity. From this point on, add variety by sometimes changing the mode or activity to keep things interesting.

When to contact a doctor or refer on

Even though we are talking about apparently healthy adults in this section, there may be times when you will ask your client to visit their doctor. You need to be aware of signs and symptoms, such as unusual and prolonged pain, that may indicate a problem. As always, you should never diagnose a condition, even if you suspect something specific – this should only be done by a qualified health care practitioner.

Qualifications

There is no specific course to recommend here as your basic instructor course will have covered the complete beginner. The main problem in this area, as highlighted above, is the need to be able to regress exercises enough for someone who has never exercised before. Personal trainers tend to focus on progression, so you will need to be creative to find ways to bring exercises down to lower and lower levels. You may find a course such as the YMCA's Disability module useful, not because people with disabilities are beginners (that would be a ridiculous assumption!), but simply because a course like that forces you to adapt your knowledge to different limitations you may come across. Similarly, the Older Adult course (run by many providers) will give you some of those tools as well.

Marketing

When considering any kind of marketing to beginners, the most important thing to be aware of are the barriers they face when starting a new exercise regime. The more accessible and approachable you are the better; if you can de-mystify the whole fitness 'thing' for someone who might be quite apprehensive about the process, the more likely you are to succeed.

Barriers might include:

- people not considering themselves to be 'sporty'
- lack of understanding about what it might entail to become fitter
- lack of knowledge about what constitutes a good trainer
- previous negative experiences of exercise
- money
- time.

The last two are apparent barriers for many people, but can actually be more about priority than anything else. We all have 24 hours in a day, so people who have been sedentary have simply not apportioned any of their time towards physical activity. When you are designing your marketing campaigning, try to address some or all of these issues.

Older adults

Overview/must know

Many organisations (the World Health Organisation, Age Concern and so on) classify older adults as being over 50 years old. This accounts for over 35 per cent of the UK population, or 20 million people. They hold 70 per cent of the UK's disposable income, so do not write them off as potential clients. In addition to the functional benefits gained by regular physical activity, a regular exercise programme also assists in reducing disease risk factors, such as diabetes and hypertension.

Exercise considerations

Psychological/social issues

Older people suffer bereavement on a more regular basis than the general population. As friends and relatives die, this can lead to feelings of isolation and depression in some people. You need to be sensitive to your client's feelings. They may start to feel vulnerable, lonely and depressed, for example. Encouraging your client to remain positive, using the techniques mentioned in the section on depression (pages 120–21) and referring on to a specialist such as a therapist or bereavement counsellor where necessary will all help.

Physical issues

There are many changes that occur with age. Fortunately, most of these do not prevent us from being physically active. On the contrary, many of the 'symptoms' of growing older (the functional decline) are preventable through exercise. Here is a list of some of the physical changes you need to be aware of:

- co-ordination, balance, hearing and sight all decline with age;
- joints are stiffer and more vulnerable because of a decrease in the amount and viscosity of synovial fluid, more fibrous cartilage, more and less supple connective tissue and stiffer ligaments;
- the cardiovascular system is not as efficient due to a reduced capillary network, arterial walls being tougher and less stretchy, lungs and respiratory tissue being less elastic and the heart being a less efficient pump;
- muscles are weaker due to the appearance of fewer fibres, a decrease in elasticity, muscle protein changes, neuromuscular realignment and less efficient delivery of oxygen to the mitochondria. In addition, loss of muscle mass (sarcopenia) is associated with lack of skeletal muscle.

Exercise recommendations

- Emphasise functional activities in your workout.
- Exercise programmes should focus on strength, flexibility, joint range of motion, balance and co-ordination.
- Remember that older adults respond well to education. They like to know why they are doing specific exercises.
- Be creative with your use of equipment. Chair work is very useful, as is using simple equipment like bands, foam balls (for gaining hand strength) and light hand-weights.
- Remember that socialisation is of huge importance to the well-being of older adults. Including time to talk, using music and having fun are vital to the retention of older adults in an exercise regime.
- Ensure a longer warm-up to allow for joint lubrication and to allow the body temperature to rise steadily.
- Offer more specific mobility work in the warm-up to prepare joints more thoroughly.
- Do not stop while stretching in the warm-up. Make sure you keep moving while stretching to keep the body warm and avoid stiffness.
- Increase and decrease the pulse throughout the session in a more graduated manner to avoid unnecessary physical stress, anaerobic work or blood pooling.
- When working aerobically, allow for a longer cool-down because older people have a less efficient cardiovascular system.
- Take care with floor-based exercises. They should not be incorporated into the main body of your workout, but should follow a gradual cool-down to take the heart rate down gently. Also, take care if you have any concern about osteoporosis being present. Even sit-ups can cause small spinal fractures in some cases.
- Always show older adults a method of getting down to the floor and back up again.

Many people find this very awkward and are afraid that once they get down, they will not be able to get back up again.
- All movement should be slow and controlled because of lack of strength and slower reaction times.
- Target minor joints that may be affected by arthritis. This will include fingers, wrists and toes.
- Avoid fast changes of direction and weight until you know the capabilities of your client.

In the UK, there are no evidence-based guidelines for exercise for the older adult. However, normal ACSM recommendations for older people are:

- 55/65–90 per cent MHR to improve cardiovascular fitness. This should be carried out 3–5 days per week for 20–60 minutes. This activity can be carried out cumulatively.
- Older adults should participate in strength work (including balance work) twice a week.

When to contact a doctor or refer on

If new to exercise, older adults should always consult their GP before starting to train with you.

Qualifications

Many training providers offer Older Adult Courses, which can range from one-day workshops to four-day courses with a recognised award at the end. During longer courses you should learn in detail about the physical and psychological changes that occur with age (including medical conditions associated with ageing) and you will also learn how to adapt exercises and programmes to suit this population.

Marketing

There are many misconceptions about age. Younger people often think of 'older people' as one homogenous group that is relatively inactive and not interested in physical activity. However, nothing could be further from the truth! If you think about older people as being over 50 (which is young to be old!), within that age group there are hugely varying levels of health status, functional ability, style and levels of energy. Just as we know people who are old when they are 20, we also know people who are 60 and full of beans. Think about it, people like Sting and Chrissie Hynde fall into the under-55 category and Paul McCartney, Joanna Lumley and Mick Jagger fall into the 56–65 age group.

You therefore need to decide on your target group. One way to break down the range is by physical ability. Spirduso breaks this down very neatly:

- physically dependent: cannot execute basic activities of daily living (BADL)
- physically frail: can perform BADL but cannot live independently
- physically independent: can live independently but with low health and fitness reserves
- physically fit: exercises twice weekly or more for health, enjoyment and well-being
- physically elite: exercises daily or works in a physically demanding job (Spirduso, 1995).

Each level will need a very different approach, both in marketing and in exercise programming. So, in thinking about your marketing messages or how you can reach older adults, you also need to think about exploding some of the myths such as 'older people are desperate to be young again'. Actually, this is not true. They are, however, looking for good health. They live by fewer rules and, in many ways, life is better than it was before. Do they only respond to price? Well, no. Older people generally have a more sophisticated concept of value, so driving down your price to be the cheapest is not necessarily the strongest message to give in attracting older people to your client base.

As with all members of the community, there will be barriers to overcome in selling fitness. However, the barriers can be much greater for the older age group. For example:

- exercise is not in their 'culture'
- they may not have been physically active for a long time and therefore have to overcome fear and inertia to get moving again
- they may not be aware of the benefits – however, it is still possible to build muscle strength well into your 90s
- they don't see themselves as a 'sporty' group
- our society encourages people to 'grow old gracefully' and it is expected that people slow down – however, people don't know that many of the effects of ageing can be massively slowed down just by taking some exercise
- there is an image of fitness and health clubs being solely for young people – we in the industry have been telling them that for years and now we need to change the tune.

Taking everything into consideration, when designing your marketing materials or methods you will need to consider the following:

- Consider your use of images so as not to stereotype the 'older population'. For example, using photos of frail elderly people exercising in chairs may not do anything to attract the active 55-year-old executive!
- Most people see themselves as 10–15 years younger than they actually are, so do not patronise!
- Educate as well as advertise. Older people respond well to education, plus you need to counteract all the problems above.
- Relate your message to Activities of Daily Living. Their motivation will be different to your 20–30-year-olds.
- Use larger print and bright colours.
- Key words will be different to a younger group. For example, 'weight loss' and 'get fit' will possibly not strike such a chord as 'feel better' or 'meet new people' for the older adult.

Medical conditions

Each condition listed contains an overview of general background information. The exercise considerations section of each population highlights the things you need to take account of and may alert you to specific risks. Finally, each section contains exercise recommendations.

Charging/funding

As with specialists in any line of work, you can potentially charge more if you choose to focus on one area and become an expert in your chosen field – think about specialist heart surgeons or dentists who specialise in cosmetic dentistry. If you do want to dedicate yourself to the medical side of personal training, it may be possible to access funding or link yourself up to funded referral schemes. This can be a good addition to your private client business and can give you some regular work if you need that kind of stability. In addition, many trainers find that getting into this field is hugely rewarding and mentally stimulating.

As mentioned above, this section is a tiny example of the kind of areas you could specialise in. Medical areas where exercise professionals can make an impact include: frail elderly people; postural stability work; pre-/post-operative; cardiac rehabilitation; and other disease-specific specialities, such as stroke, HIV, cancer and so on.

Exercise on referral

With the advent of GP Referral Schemes around the country, a whole new interest has appeared in working with medically referred clients. Developing formal partnerships with GPs and clinicians can be a very attractive prospect and seem like a very worthwhile way to use your skills. However, you must take the cultural viewpoint into consideration, that is the differing cultures of the medical profession and the NHS compared with yours as an entrepreneurial person needing to earn a living. You may well find that NHS doctors seem unwilling to refer patients to you if you are going to make a profit from them. In their minds, it goes against all the principles of equity. If you are truly going to make this system work for you, it may be better to work through private clinicians instead. There will be less of a cultural difference and you will reach clients with the means to pay for your services.

There is also the possibility of funding or attaching yourself to a scheme that is funded. Many Primary Care Trusts (PCTs) around the country fund medical referral schemes in their community. Some of these schemes make use of personal trainers, which allows you to use your skills with very different clients from the ones you might generally find come to you on a more commercial basis.

If this is the area of work you are particularly interested in, there are several factors you need to consider. Your qualifications need to reflect the client group with which you want to work. You need to be able to prove competence with whomever you choose to work. Refer to REPs (see page 143 for contact details) for advice as to acceptable qualifications at Level 3.

The best way to start this sort of system or specialisation is to thoroughly think through all the implications and your systems in advance of approaching any clinicians. Here is a checklist for you to go through:

Undertake a thorough risk assessment

Where will you work with clients? If it is in a gym or studio setting, what are the emergency protocols there? Is there a phone with an outside line you can access quickly? Are there emergency buttons located strategically around the building should someone become ill while they are with you? Are there other first-aiders available as well as yourself? Do you have access to a defibrillator (this one is by no means essential, but can be a selling point to clinicians should it be available and may be an issue if you choose to specialise in, for example, cardiac rehabilitation)? If you will be working with clients in their homes or outside, you will need to assess the risks for each environment in relation to the types of clients you will be working with.

Decide on your systems

Will you be setting up a formal system or asking clinicians to recommend exercise? The latter is more simple to administer, but you will not have such formal lines of communication with a clinician and will therefore not have access to client medical histories or have easy access to the referrer should you have any concerns or questions.

If you choose to use the recommendation system, there will be no further work needed in this area. However, if you choose the referral system, you will need to decide what sort of clients you will target and whether you are going to accept any medical condition or specialise in a particular one. Develop a list of those patients you will and won't accept. For example, you will need to list those patients who you will not take under any circumstances, such as those with uncontrolled medical conditions or those you are not qualified to deal with. Even if you choose to specialise in a particular area, such as cardiac rehabilitation, you will still need to list those patients within this category who would be unsuitable for an exercise programme. Within a particular area, those who might be contraindicated to exercise would have very specific conditions and you will need to be aware of these. So, for example, within cardiac rehab. this might include unstable angina or a recent complicated myocardial infarction (heart attack). You will need to design a referral form, detailing the information you require from the doctor. This may include relevant medical history, medication, any exercise the referrer does not want you to do, the referrer's goals or aims and the reason for referral. Give some thought too as to the transfer of information. Will the referrer send the form to you and then you contact their patient, or will it be up to the patient to contact you directly? If the latter is the case, then perhaps a letter of introduction to the patient might be a good idea, so that they know how to contact you, what your charges are, what will be expected of them, where they will train and so on.

Confidentiality

You need to realise that confidentiality is of the utmost importance when dealing with an individual's personal medical information. As a personal trainer, you will be used to this as an issue anyway, but do give extra special attention to this area. Will you be keeping any medical information on computer? If so, give some thought to data protection. If you work in a gym setting, what information, if any, will be kept on site? If it is to be kept on site, no one should have access to it but you or other personnel working on the referral scheme. It goes without saying that you should never discuss any personal information relating to clients at any time.

Payment

This will largely be dependent upon the type of system you have set up and whether or not you are funded. If you are taking private clients through referral from private referrers, you may wish to have a set fee not unlike what you charge regular clients. If, on the other hand, you are taking clients from NHS sources, you may find that you have to modify your charges. In this case, it is important not to set people up to fail. If you lower your fees for a set number of sessions or period of time, what happens when that period expires? If the target group cannot afford your regular fees, you need to think up some exit strategy. For example, you could give them the tools they need to exercise safely and effectively on their own and then refer them on to local opportunities for physical activity, such as group activities or perhaps a local leisure centre. Alternatively, you could offer a follow-up service whereby you coach clients by phone, allowing them to check in with you periodically while maintaining an exercise programme alone. While this seems to go against the interests of most personal trainers, where the aim is to keep people as clients for as long as possible, this kind of system does allow you to 'give something back'. It can be hugely rewarding and a viable adjunct to a busy personal training practice. Medical referrals are very satisfying and an interesting break from the norm.

Feedback to referrer

Whether you train referred clients on an ongoing basis or for a short period of time, it is always a good idea to periodically give feedback to the referrer, otherwise they will have no idea whether the scheme works or whether their patients are benefiting. This feedback may simply take the from of a short note or letter telling the referrer that the client has completed three months of exercise and giving some results if known. Bear in mind that formal fitness testing information probably has little meaning to most GPs or medics. Instead, think in terms of functional assessment information. Information regarding a person's ability to cope with the demands of everyday living will be very useful for both client and referrer alike.

Partnerships

Working with referred populations obviously requires that you develop a partnership agreement with medical practitioners. For many fitness professionals this can be a daunting prospect at first. Making the initial contact can sometimes be the hardest part and it is therefore worth starting with someone you already know, perhaps even your own GP or private specialist. Make sure you have thought about your systems and how you will run the partnership. Most doctors are very busy people. They have well over 100 different routes for referral of their patients and they don't have time to decide on the detail of this sort of agreement. Make sure you come armed with evidence about how exercise and physical activity can benefit his or her patients. As a fitness professional you may be well aware of just how many conditions exercise can help with, but doctors are scientists and they always need evidence, so do your research. You will also need to prove your qualifications and that you know how to look after their patients.

Depending on your level of experience, it is probably a good idea to start with 'low-risk' patients, that is patients who have a medical condition that is not so serious that you will need to be highly specialised in your exercise prescription. This will include patients suffering with things like mild to moderate depression, or patients who are overweight or obese but have no other cardiac risk factors, and so on.

We will now look at a few medical conditions in a little more detail. Never be afraid to refer back if necessary. If you are unsure about anything or if you observe or discover something about your client that causes you any concern regarding their safety or their ability to exercise, ask permission from your client to contact their doctor for clarification.

Diabetes

Overview/must know

Diabetes is a chronic metabolic disease whereby the body produces insufficient or no insulin. This hormone, secreted by the pancreas, enables glucose to be taken up by the body's cells. In the non-diabetic, insulin is released when blood sugar levels are elevated, thus reducing blood sugar to normal levels again. For the person with diabetes, the lack of insulin can leave blood sugar levels dangerously high or low.

In the UK, as in other Western countries, diabetes is a growing and serious problem. To date, over 2 million people in the UK have been diagnosed with the disease (Diabetes UK) and a quarter of all people with diabetes are undiagnosed. The disease can lead to increased risk of heart disease, stroke, kidney disease, amputations and blindness.

Type I (insulin-dependent) diabetes usually occurs in younger individuals and affects 10–15 per cent of people with diabetes. Treatment is usually via regular insulin injections. Type II (adult-onset or non-insulin-dependent) diabetes generally occurs in adults. Type II is far more prevalent. Although a genetic predisposition can increase the likelihood of developing type II diabetes, obesity can be one of the biggest causes of the disease. Treatment for this type of diabetes is usually a combination of weight reduction, controlled diet and oral medication.

Benefits of exercise

Exercise can help in the prevention and treatment of diabetes in several ways. These include:

- an improvement in blood cholesterol profile
- cardiovascular benefits – this is important because diabetics are more prone to developing heart disease
- stress management – this is an important part of care for the diabetic client
- lower blood pressure
- improved insulin sensitivity and, therefore, possible reduction in the need for or amount of medication
- possible improvement in blood glucose control – this occurs in people with type II diabetes
- decreased body fat – weight loss also increases insulin sensitivity.

Exercise considerations

It is imperative that you screen your client and get medical clearance before embarking on a training programme with them. The person's diabetic condition must be stable. That is, their blood sugar levels must be maintained at normal levels by medication, insulin or diet.

It is important to ensure that your client does not go hypoglycaemic (low blood sugar) during the exercise session. They should be directed to eat 1–2 hours before exercising and even possibly to eat a small snack just before the session. After longer training sessions, they should eat some slowly absorbed carbohydrates such as porridge, pasta or apples. In addition, ensure that your client checks their blood glucose level directly before exercising. If you meet them in a gym setting, make sure there is somewhere private for them to do this. Make sure you know the symptoms of hypoglycaemia. These include excessive fatigue or feeling faint, light-headedness, sweating, irritability and slurred speech. Ultimately, they may have a seizure or lose consciousness.

Those who are new to exercise should work closely with their diabetic nurse to ensure the balance of medication (timing and dose) and food intake work with the new exercise regime.

Diabetes can cause damage to the nerves in the legs and feet (diabetic neuropathy). If your client suffers with this they may not feel pain, heat or cold in their feet. Diabetics can also suffer with poor circulation in this area, meaning that cuts and sores take longer to heal. Ensure your client looks after their feet by checking them regularly and wearing good quality, appropriate shoes. If they suffer with neuropathy, be aware of potential balance issues and also be aware that injury to the feet may not be felt by the client.

Exercise recommendations

- Both aerobic and resistance programmes are appropriate for diabetic clients. Where appropriate, the focus should be on exercise to promote weight loss.
- Blood sugar levels are best controlled through steady state, predictable aerobic activity.
- Exercise programmes must be individualised to take into account any complications, medication and timing of medication and goals.
- Always carry glucose tablets or some other fast-acting carbohydrate or juice while training.
- Ensure fluid intake is sufficient.
- Avoid exercise in the late evening.
- Do not exercise any muscle directly underneath the site of insulin injection for at least one hour after injection. The insulin may be absorbed too quickly and could bring on hypoglycaemia.

When to contact a doctor or refer on

Absolute contraindications to exercise for diabetic clients according to ACSM, Exercise Management for Persons with Chronic diseases and disabilities, include:

- Where there has been recent therapy for retinopathy or where active retinal haemorrhage is present.
- If the client has any illness or infection. You would not necessarily refer back to the doctor in this case; it would just be wise not to exercise for the duration of the illness.
- If the client has very high (>250 mgdl) or very low (<100mgdl) blood glucose levels. Remember, the diabetic client should be stable before they begin a programme with you.

Qualifications

Training diabetic clients will come into a GP Referral course. These are generally five-day courses and diabetes will be only one of a number of conditions covered.

Weight management

Overview/must know

Overweight and obesity is on the increase across the developed world. Obesity can be defined as an excess of body fat to the extent that it adversely affects health. In the UK alone over half of all adults are overweight and almost a quarter are obese. Obesity is a serious medical condition that increases risk for coronary heart disease, diabetes, hypertension, hyperlipidemia and hormone and menstrual dysfunction. Obesity also increases severity of disease.

What is obesity?

Obesity is measured in two ways: Body Mass Index (BMI) and waist circumference. BMI is weight (kilos) divided by height (metres squared). Table 9.1 shows how the World Health Organisation categorises over- or underweight according to BMI.

Table 9.1	Body mass index
Underweight	≤ 18.5
Healthy weight	18.6–24.9
Overweight	25–29.9
Obese	≥ 30

It must be noted that BMI does not take into consideration the difference between weight that is fat and weight that is muscular in nature. To this end, many athletes come out with a very high BMI level, which would put them into the obese category. Clearly this is not the case and common sense must prevail in looking at measurements like this.

The way body fat is distributed can indicate increased risk. Men tend to store fat more around the abdomen, which indicates greater risk of mortality and morbidity than fat stored below the hips (more common in women). Therefore, the second measure for obesity is hip to waist ratio and, more recently, waist circumference. Hip to waist ratio should be below 0.8 for women and below 1 for men (ACSM, 2005). Table 9.2 indicates how waist circumference can be used to indicate the level of risk to a person's health (Association for the Study of Obesity, 2005).

Table 9.2	Waist circumference	
	Increased risk	*Substantial risk*
Men	> 94 cm	> 102 cm
Women	> 80 cm	> 88 cm

Weight loss is probably the single biggest reason for formal referral in most GP referral schemes. The slimming industry in general is far more successful at tapping into this market than the fitness industry, yet we know that exercise and diet together are the best solutions for most people in their efforts to lose weight.

However, this category could come into normal populations as well as referred clients. All you need to decide is where you want to focus. The issues are the same. A huge number of potential clients will be battling the weight issue and if you specialise in this area, you are assured a constant stream of customers. Your clients would therefore be people who are obese, overweight, or of normal weight but who struggle to maintain that size. The obese category is where there is a much greater risk of disease and ill health. As a personal trainer, you may choose to specialise in this area, which will take you into the clinical realm if that is your interest. However, there is also a huge market in the weight loss area for people who are of normal weight but struggle to stay there and those who are overweight, but not to the extent it would damage health. Undoubtedly, there are some individuals who are genetically predisposed to gain weight, but for most people the struggle is more about the fact that our environment almost discourages daily activity. Add to this the easy availability of junk food and the difficulty many people have in sticking to a healthy diet, and it is easy to see how we have got ourselves into this position.

Benefits of exercise

Exercise can have a significant effect on overweight, although where a person has a BMI over 40 success may be more limited and medical intervention (invasive) would be the most likely first line of treatment. The process of weight loss is a complicated one, but certainly regular sustained aerobic activity will help decrease body fat by increasing energy expenditure. The behavioural change involved in increasing physical activity could also have an effect on other positive behaviours such as becoming more aware of dietary intake. Success in losing weight is more likely if a three-pronged attack is made: physical activity, diet/nutrition and behavioural change. If you do not have the necessary skills in all areas, it might be a good idea to refer your client to relevant professionals for the other area(s).

Many clients will hope that you can solve their problems and reduce their body fat in the specific areas that they want to work on. This cannot be done and you must make it clear to your clients what is and isn't possible. Each person's ability to lose fat and from where is individual and is not something they are able to influence. Instead, programming focus should be on adherence to physical activity, so the client's enjoyment and sense of mastery is crucial. In addition, they should understand the principle of energy expenditure such that if they burn more calories than they ingest, they will lose weight. To this end, what they do between sessions is also crucial to their success. Anything that can influence this decision on a daily basis should be attempted. Use of a simple pedometer, for example, can be a great way of motivating people to be more active. It is easy to use and gives a clear indication of when the individual has achieved their daily target.

Psychology

There is a commonly held view that people who are overweight lack self-discipline and are lazy. This can have a devastating effect on people who have suffered with weight issues for long periods of time. Be aware that overweight or obese people can therefore suffer significant barriers to taking part in a physical activity programme. These include previous negative experiences, particularly where the weight problem has been in existence for a long time, or embarrassment about their body shape. Always be sympathetic to such barriers and offer solutions such as exercising at home, emphasising activities that are more functional, such as walking, and exercise that can be done in 'normal' clothing. In addition, constant encouragement and the setting of small achievable goals will help your client to feel that they are succeeding. Steer away from trying to get clients to hit the nationally recognised targets for health or fitness, such as 10,000 steps per day or 30 minutes of moderate physical activity on most days of the week. By all means they should use a pedometer as this can be effective in getting people more active, as discussed above. However, they might not be advised to go for 10,000 steps per day as their initial target. For many people, this goal will simply be unachievable and off-putting. Instead, if they are currently only doing one or two thousand steps per day, add the number of daily steps in small increments so that they can mark their achievements and stay motivated. Keeping the exercise prescription personal and increasing the level gradually will be far more effective for most people. Your client's enjoyment is key in this area.

Other barriers can be the level of discomfort experienced by moving while carrying the extra weight, the lack of momentum associated with being overweight and the expectations of other people. Those closest to the client may be threatened by their success if they were to lose weight, so social support and choosing the right people for this is really important. See page 83 for more on this.

When setting goals, it is also important to keep them realistic. In terms of the health benefits that can be attained through weight loss, clients should be advised that 10 per cent of total body weight is the optimum level that people should aim for in the long term. This is fine with clients who are moderately overweight and can help you to work with them to re-define issues over body image and what is acceptable to them. Unfortunately, most people who are obese want to lose a lot more than this. The trouble with having an impractical weight loss goal means that whatever success is achieved can be ignored and the client can go into a spiral of negativity regarding their efforts. Instead of celebrating their success, they feel they have failed and then become unwilling to continue in their effort.

Diet

Clients who struggle with weight loss will inevitably look to you for dietary advice as well as for exercise and it would be foolish to ignore the issue of food. However, unless you are specifically qualified in this area, you must stick to general advice and help only. Your clients may have lost weight in the past on specific diets and have questions about the various fad diets available. The truth is that, in the broadest sense, all diets work. By this I mean that they all help you lose weight. If you consume fewer calories than you expend, you will lose weight. The main issues, then, are whether a diet helps people to remain at a healthier weight in the longer term and whether it is indeed safe or healthy. When people want to lose weight, they frequently ignore health and safety in their quest: diet is not only important in the weight issue, but also impacts on general health concerns such as cardiovascular health, blood pressure, bone health, cancers and well-being. It is therefore crucial that you encourage a diet that is generally healthy and give advice that will help people to stick to their dietary goals while you focus on the physical activity.

People who lose weight generally regain one

third of that weight after one year and by year five they will be almost back to their pre-weight-loss weight. Commercial weight loss organisations such as Weight Watchers, Slimmers World and Rosemary Conley are usually successful in helping with weight loss for the duration that people attend and this may be a useful add-on for your clients to do in addition to their personal training sessions. Indeed, the health care profession is increasingly working with these organisations because of the success that weekly support sessions provide.

General advice

- Avoid food that is high in saturated fat, salt and refined carbohydrates.
- Eat more fruit and vegetables, whole grains, nuts and seeds, low-fat dairy products, lean meat and fish.
- Limit alcohol intake.
- Choose carbohydrates with a low glycaemic index.
- Reduce portion sizes.
- Eat regular meals.
- Plan snacks in advance and, if necessary, carry them with you.
- Eat breakfast.

Exercise considerations

Due to the number of other medical conditions that may be present when someone is overweight or obese, caution must be exercised when training these clients and also when carrying out fitness assessments. Medical clearance would be a wise precaution, but bear in mind that in the UK patients will be unlikely to undertake an exercise tolerance test unless there has been some history of heart complaint or disease.

In your initial assessment, it is useful to take some baseline measures to help with exercise prescription. It will be important to find out a client's history in terms of previous attempts to lose weight and how long weight has been an issue. If someone has only been overweight as an adult and has not fluctuated in weight over a period of time, they are more likely to be successful in their attempt.

Be sensitive when assessing body composition. The use of callipers may not be recommended with this client group as it could be demotivating and also may be perceived as being a humiliating exercise. In addition, the measurements may not be accurate and would only serve to tell the client what they already know. Simple circumference measurements may be a smarter move and could be highly motivating as clients watch their size decrease over the weeks.

The ultimate goal for a client who wants to lose weight is to decrease fat weight while increasing or maintaining lean tissue. Stored body fat contains 7000 calories per kg. Therefore, a 500-calorie daily deficit would be needed to lose 0.5 kg per week. It is easy to see, therefore, that an average weight loss of 0.5–1 kg per week should be achievable for most people and allow them to be consistent in the exercise and dietary changes needed to achieve that level of weight loss. The body is generally unable to lose more than 1 kg of fat weight per week, which is why at weight loss faster than this individuals start to lose lean tissue.

The main exercise considerations in obese adults are injury prevention and thermoregulation (ACSM). When a person is carrying excess weight, there is considerable pressure on the joints and exercise could exacerbate existing problems here.

Remember too that most pieces of gym equipment have a maximum weight allowance, so always check this before using any. Also be sensitive to size and comfort as some seats may not be large enough to accommodate your client. The same issue may occur when you take their blood pressure; ensure you have a large enough cuff size to allow for your clients.

Exercise recommendations

If your client has a serious weight issue, it is imperative that they are encouraged to increase physical activity on a daily basis. Sessions with you should then focus on more specific conditioning. The primary goal is clearly to expend more calories while minimising risk of injury. As mentioned previously, though, if a person has been doing little or no physical activity up to this time, emphasis must be placed on enjoyment and activities of daily living.

The ACSM recommends resistance training plus non-weight-bearing activities in addition to walking and other activities of daily living. Activity should take place on at least five days of the week at relatively low intensity (50–70 per cent maximal oxygen consumption) for 40–60 minutes. Exercise bouts can be taken in one session or split over two.

Qualifications

Weight management will be covered in the broadest terms in many basic gym courses. Nutrition and weight management courses are available through many providers. Obesity courses are currently offered by two providers: Lifetime and The Wright Foundation (see pages 143 and 144 for contact details).

Hypertension

Overview/must know

Hypertension simply means high blood pressure. Blood pressure is cardiac output, or the amount of blood pumped around the body multiplied by the resistance measure in the arteries. A normal blood pressure reading would be around 120/80 (< 130 systolic and < 85 diastolic). The top figure refers to the pressure during the heart's pumping phase (systolic) and the lower figure represents the relaxed phase (diastolic). Blood pressure is said to be high when it measures over 140/90.

Hypertension is a condition that largely presents without symptoms. 38 per cent of men and 32 per cent of women are known to be hypertensive (Health Survey for England 2003, Department of Health). The real figure, however, is probably much higher as many adults remain undiagnosed.

The cause of hypertension is largely unknown. However, several lifestyle factors are known to exacerbate the condition and are known risk factors. These include physical inactivity, smoking, excessive sodium and alcohol intake and stress. Other factors that could predispose someone to hypertension are family history, age, sex and high cholesterol. To this end, when working with a hypertensive client it is worth advising that other lifestyle changes are made, such as losing weight (where applicable), limiting alcohol intake, reducing the amount of salt and saturated fat in the diet and smoking cessation.

Benefits of exercise

Elevated blood pressure in itself is a risk factor for cardiovascular disease and renal disease. Risk of these and all-cause mortality increases as blood pressure gets higher (ACSM). Exercise can be an extremely effective intervention for this condition. It can reduce hypertension and increase mental well-being. The main priorities will be weight loss (if your client is overweight) and stress management.

Exercise considerations

If a client has been diagnosed with hypertension, be sure to ask them to see their GP before embarking on an exercise programme. Uncontrolled hypertension is an absolute contraindication to exercise and you should not train anyone under these conditions. In addition, exercise should not be undertaken if systolic blood pressure is greater than 200 mmHg or diastolic blood pressure is greater than 115 mmHg.

The most important consideration is always safety, and you need assurance that there is no other medical complication that may indicate a contraindication to exercise.

In addition, you need to be aware of any medication your client may be taking. Blood pressure medications can affect the exercise response and you need to be able to deal with this. Medication for this condition falls into specific types. When you find out the name of a drug, you then need to find the generic name to discover which family of drugs it falls into. Main drug groups for hypertension are:

Beta blockers

These lower the pulse rate and can cause tiredness, cold extremities, postural hypotension, fatigue, depression and dizziness. The reduced heart rate (and heart rate response to exercise) mean that the use of heart rate monitoring to measure exercise intensity is ill advised. Use the Borg Scale instead (see pages 89–90). In addition, because hypotension (low blood pressure) is a risk for people taking beta blockers, care should be taken when rising from the floor and when going from sitting to standing. Avoid stopping exercise very suddenly and allow more time for the cool-down.

ACE inhibitors

These can cause dizziness, a dry cough and headaches.

Angiotensin II antagonists

These can cause dizziness. Again, care should be taken when rising from the floor or a chair.

Diuretics

These can cause dehydration, tiredness, aching limbs and muscular weakness. Ensure your client is adequately hydrated and continues to take on fluids while exercising. Use more caution in excessive heat.

Calcium channel blockers (calcium antagonists)

These can cause headaches, dizziness, faintness and stomach problems. They can also reduce the heart rate response to exercise and therefore the Borg scale (pages 89–90) should be used to assess exercise intensity.

Alpha blockers

These can cause headaches, postural hypotension, dizziness, vertigo and fatigue. Use the recommendations given above.

As you can see, there are a lot of side effects to take into consideration. However, the side effects are similar even for different drugs. You must also bear in mind that not everybody will have the same reactions to drugs. You should therefore always check with your client to see how they are feeling and responding.

Exercise recommendations

Exercise should be taken on a regular basis, so leave your clients with weekly goals for daily activity such as walking or cycling. They should be physically active for a minimum of three days per week, but should aim for daily activity if possible. Clients should build up to exercising for at least 20 minutes during every exercise session with the ultimate aim of regularly working for 20–60 minutes at a time. Exercise recommendations are similar to those for the general healthy population and so intensity is recommended at 50–85 per cent maximum oxygen consumption. However, lower intensities do appear to elicit a similar blood pressure lowering response and may be advisable where your client is unable to work at a higher intensity (ACSM).

Follow these general principles:

- Focus on moderate, predictable and rhythmic aerobic activity using large muscle groups.
- Resistance training should be done with low weights and high repetitions.
- Isometric exercises should be avoided.
- Do not put your client into positions where their feet are raised above their head, such as on an incline bench.
- In resistance exercise, decrease the load and reps in exercises when the arms are raised over the head.
- Advise your client to breathe throughout the exercise session. Remind them not to hold their breath, for example, when resistance training or when stretching.
- Allow for a longer warm-up and cool-down.

Terminate the exercise session if any of the following occur:

- excessive fatigue
- light-headedness
- nausea
- anginal pain
- sudden drop in heart rate (greater than 10 beats per minute) with no corresponding reduction in exercise intensity.

When to contact a doctor or refer on

When you take on your client, you may decide to measure blood pressure as part of the fitness assessment. Whatever reading you get, you must remember that it is not your job to diagnose high blood pressure. Only a medical professional can do that and will only do so after measuring blood pressure on several occasions. If you get a reading that is unusually high, do try to determine why that may be the case. There are several reasons for a temporarily high reading such as just after eating, drinking coffee and stress.

Qualifications

Rather like diabetes, hypertension will be covered in a couple of courses but will only be one part of those courses. Both GP Referral Courses and the British Association of Cardiac Rehab. Phase IV course will cover this area.

Depression

Overview/must know

One in six people will experience depression at some point in their lives and women are far more likely to suffer with it than men (The Mental Health Foundation). While early experiences can be a causal factor in depression, genetics are also of great relevance in predicting who will suffer with it.

Bear in mind that we are not just talking about feeling a bit 'down' here, but diagnosed depression. People who are depressed experience overwhelming feelings of sadness and clients may lack motivation, feel tired (TATT – tired all the time), lack concentration and appear negative. They can feel like everything is hopeless and suffer with low self-esteem. When someone is suffering with severe depression they will lack the motivation to do anything at all. They will probably need medical intervention before they would even consider exercising. You are most likely to see people with mild to moderate depression, and this is the group that exercise would benefit the most anyway. If you have a client whom you suspect may be suffering with depression, it is likely they will start to cancel sessions or not show up.

Benefits of exercise

There is now a plethora of research (Biddle et al., 2000 and Department of Health, 2004) advocating physical activity as being beneficial to mental health in general and in particular with depression. It has been shown to lead to the following:

- mood improvement
- improved self-concept
- decreased depression/anxiety
- fewer feelings of anger and confusion.

Exercise is now recommended in the treatment of patients who are mildly to moderately depressed and they should start to feel better within 3–5 weeks of starting an exercise programme, although the greatest benefits will be felt after 17 weeks.

Exercise considerations

Bear in mind that anti-depressant medication can lead to insomnia, weight gain and dizziness. You will also need to work hard to keep your client motivated and will need to exercise patience, as being around someone who is clinically depressed can be hard work. Your client may experience poor levels of concentration, so be prepared to repeat simple instructions and to be tolerant in your approach.

Exercise recommendations

No specific exercise guidelines exist for people who suffer with depression and so the recommendations are the same as for any healthy adult. However, exercise will be more beneficial in mood enhancement if sessions are taken on a regular basis; clients should therefore be advised to exercise at least three times per week.

It does not appear to make any difference whether the exercise sessions are aerobically based or not. All types of exercise appear to have an anti-depressive effect. However, many people seem to find steady state, predictable exercise such as jogging, swimming and cycling can have a calming effect.

Qualifications

No formal qualification exists for training clients with depression and you do not really need to be able to prove competence in this area. The only course available is the YMCA's Exercise and Activity in Mental Health, which is a one-day module.

PSYCHOLOGY AND MOTIVATION 10

In this chapter you will:

- discover the secrets of motivating your clients
- understand the psychology behind behaviour change.

As you will have seen throughout this book, attaining the technical skills you need to train your clients is really only half the story – getting your clients to adhere to their exercise programme is one of the biggest challenges you will face, and the real trick for keeping your clients working hard is in the psychology. Let's take, for example, a new client. Not new to exercise, she has tried (and failed) to stick with an exercise plan for years. She tried joining a gym, but found she was paying out loads of money for her membership each month but in reality hardly ever going. The problem was, she found the gym boring. Also, let's face it, most things about getting fit and being physically active are actually quite painful for most people; getting sweaty and increasing the heart rate and respiration rate are not the most comfortable of feelings. This client has now come to you and wants you to motivate her.

This is probably the biggest single issue for every personal trainer: clients want to be motivated and they want you to do it. When they fail to comply with your instructions, they blame you for not getting results! Therefore, you need to work skilfully with your clients so that they actually motivate themselves. This means taking on the role of coach as well as that of a trainer.

Behaviour change

Goal setting

Helping your client achieve their goals is crucial to their success and yours. However, many people find it very hard to actually set goals; many people don't really know what they want. Part of your skill as a personal trainer will be helping your client to define exactly what it is they want to achieve. In many instances, the first reason people give is not the real reason – in other words, it doesn't get to the core of their desires. Ask your client what they want and then immediately ask them what they really want. This will help them to access a deeper answer than the one they think you want to hear. See pages 81–4 for more on goal setting.

Motivating your clients

As we saw above, part of your role as a personal trainer is to help your clients to motivate themselves. Some of the techniques you can use to do this are rooted firmly in psychology, while others have merely been used in the fitness setting and appear to elicit success.

Personal responsibility

We live in a 'blame' culture. It is very easy to blame our parents, upbringing, school, partner, job, the government and so on for our current physical or other condition in life. Unfortunately, this is the way most people live their lives – it is always someone else's fault. This does not bode well for personal trainers! If your client does not get the results they want, even though you know they did not stick to your advice between sessions, they will see it as your fault. Therefore, you need to turn this around and get your client to take responsibility for their own health and fitness, making them understand that whether or not they succeed in their goals is entirely up to them. You as the trainer are there to help them along that road. In order to encourage your client to take responsibility, ensure that:

- all goals are the client's own, not yours or anyone else's
- the programme reflects the ongoing desires of your client
- the activities are ones they enjoy and have chosen themselves.

Create realistic expectations

If clients are new to exercise, they may well have unrealistic expectations about what their new exercise regime will be able to do for them. Addressing this at the start by making it clear what is and isn't possible will help to instil feelings of achievement in terms of the client's training schedule and the changes they experience as a result.

Relapse prevention

Lapse and relapse are a part of the process of behaviour change. New clients will without doubt find occasions when they are not able to exercise. This may be due to illness, pressure at work, holidays, the Christmas break and so on. Just as you help to create realistic expectations about results, it is wise to let your clients know in advance that these instances will occur. Knowing that this is a natural part of the process and planning how to tackle these short breaks in advance will help the client feel in control and therefore prevent them from giving up entirely.

Competition

This can be a good motivator for some people, although it is important that you are able to recognise when and for whom competition might be a real turn-off (see pages 77–81). In the personal training context, 'competition' will most likely mean helping your client towards something they have set up as a goal in their life, such as competing in a 10 km run. Alternatively, they could set up a challenge with a friend about total weight loss over a period of time.

The Premack Principle

One psychological technique that can be applied to the exercise setting is the 'Premack Principle'. It has the rather endearing common name of 'Grandma's rule' (Presbie and Brown, 1977) as, rather like when Grandma used to make you eat your greens before you could have dessert, it is based on the idea that you put off a pleasurable or more favourable activity until you have completed, say, your exercise session. For example, your clients could say to themselves that if they attend the gym three times a week for a month, they can treat themselves to a massage; or on one particular day, they can decide to only ring their best friend for a chat once they have completed their run. Your clients need to be strict with themselves, however, and ensure that they really don't do the pleasurable activity until they have done the work. You also need to ensure that your clients' pleasurable activities do not sabotage the efforts they make in training; if their goal is to feel better and have more energy, there is no point in making the pleasurable activity five pints of lager at the pub!

Cueing or prompting

Encourage your client to exercise by introducing the idea of using a cue. This might, for example, mean putting their running shoes by the front door so they remember to go for a run when they get in from work. You will also prompt quite naturally during training sessions with them, for example by encouraging them to keep going when they feel they can't do the last rep of a leg press set.

Variety

Sticking to the same programme for months on end will result in boredom and dropout for many people. Add variety by changing programmes, adding one new exercise per session or creating 'events' or themes.

Support

As well as the support you offer during training sessions, the support you offer between sessions such as notes, e-mails and phone calls all affect how supported your client feels, which will directly affect their motivation. Also try to get your clients to drum up support from their partner, family, friends or colleagues as this will magnify their efforts. It also makes them answerable to someone else. See also page 83.

Feedback

Showing your clients how they are improving by periodically repeating any fitness assessments or measurements will help them to keep going, especially as progress begins to slow down or plateau. On a more regular basis, you could remind them that just a short time ago they would have struggled to do what they are doing now, or get them to take their resting pulse and monitor it as it decreases over time.

Psychological models of change

As we have discussed, clients will often come to you because they want you to motivate them. They may have tried to start exercising regularly on several occasions but have been unable to sustain this. Application of your knowledge of the behaviour change models described below will help you to shape a programme and an approach that may make the difference.

Stages of Change (Prochaska and DiClemente, 1983)

Over the last few years, the 'Stages of Change' model has become increasingly popular in the physical activity arena. Originally developed for use with addictive behaviours such as smoking, the model suggests that people go through a number of stages when instigating behavioural change, taking into account both their motivation to change as well as actual change. The process is seen as cyclical because individuals can join the process at any stage, may lapse at any stage and may need to try to change the behaviour on several occasions before they are actually successful. The stages of change are:

Pre-contemplation

Here the individual sees no problem with their current behaviour and has no intention of changing. You would be unlikely to see someone at this stage in a personal training session. People at this stage are more likely to do no exercise and perhaps engage in other unhealthy behaviours such as smoking and drinking to excess. They may be apparently healthy and see no problem with continuing as they currently do. Their social life may revolve around the pub and all of their peer group may well behave in a similar way.

Contemplation

Here the individual perceives a possible threat to their health or sees some other possible problems should they continue their current lifestyle. At this point, they might start to think about adopting the new behaviour and they may weigh up the pros and cons of change versus no change. If we continue with the example above, this person's best friend has now just been diagnosed with lung cancer. They therefore no longer see themselves as invincible. You may come across someone like this in a social setting and they may appear curious about what you do. Questioning techniques can be useful here: for example, the decisional balance system on page 83 is a good tool to help people weigh up their choices of change or no change.

Preparation

The individual now starts to look into how they might adopt the new behaviour. They will start to become slightly more active, but not on a regular basis. At this point, you could help your client to move on by getting them to focus on the benefits of physical activity that they are experiencing. Work with them to find ways of making this new behaviour more regular so that it fits more easily into their life. You may also want to focus on addressing any barriers that they may be experiencing and help them to find practical solutions.

Action

The individual is now physically active. (The action stage refers to the first six months of activity only.) Work on increasing your client's confidence and help them to set longer-term fitness goals. They may need to be stimulated with new and fun ideas to avoid getting bored.

Maintenance

The individual is now physically active on a regular basis following the six-month action stage.

At some point after this, the individual would consider the new behaviour, in this case exercise, to be a part of their lifestyle and would no longer consider themselves to be inactive.

The specific technique used to move clients through the Stages of Change is known as 'Motivational Interviewing'. If you are particularly interested in this concept, it is worth taking a specific training course for this purpose. In this way you can identify where your clients are in the cycle and help them to move through the specific stages with far more skill.

Health Belief Model (Rosenstock, 1974)

The Health Belief Model is based on motivation towards preventative health behaviour. It bases the likelihood of taking preventative health action, in this case exercise, on a number of factors: first is the perceived threat and severity of disease if the individual does not exercise (as in the example above, where a person's best friend has lung cancer); second are the various triggers towards the health behaviour, such as demographics, psychology and knowledge/ experience of the disease; and the third element is how the individual weighs up the perceived benefits of taking exercise against the barriers.

According to a review of several studies, Janz and Becker found that the third element (weighing up the benefits against the barriers) was the most decisive in indicating behaviour change (Janz and Becker, 1984). However, one of the limitations of this model is that it has been suggested that it only predicts a single bout of a single behaviour (Sonstroem, 1988). The implication here is that, as exercise involves a complex set of behaviours over a period of time, the Health Belief Model may not be a good predictor of this particular preventative health behaviour. However, if you take this information and apply it in your work as a personal trainer, it does indicate that the work you do with clients towards helping them overcome barriers to regular participation in physical activity could be the most valuable. The decisional balance sheet on page 83 is again a useful tool. In addition, use the questioning techniques on pages 127–8 to identify clearly your client's specific barriers to long-term participation in physical activity. Finally, this model may have uses with people who take up exercise for health reasons.

Learning Theory (Skinner, 1953)

Skinner's Learning Theory suggests that the right conditions for exercise (for example, the client has booked sessions with you and has some new training shoes) and the experience of exercise as being enjoyable (perhaps the client enjoyed walking with their partner at the weekend) are more likely to lead to the individual continuing to be physically active in the future. The other point of note in this theory is the importance of increasing activity gradually. If you push beginners too much or if people start too enthusiastically and push themselves too hard, they are likely to drop out. Using the Learning Theory, you can therefore educate your new clients to start off at a low level. Letting them know why this is good and that they are still getting the health benefits of physical activity without having to push themselves to the limit will encourage them to stick with it. Reward and encouragement will also help your client to keep going, especially in the crucial first few months of taking up an exercise programme.

Coaching your client to success

The success or otherwise of your client will depend largely on how you set up the relationship from the beginning. Taking the time to get to know your client well – what motivates them, what makes them throw in the towel and so on – and setting up ground rules will all help to guide your client to success. The questions you ask will really make the difference here. Asking the right questions will help your client come up with answers for themselves. Let's face it, most people know what they *should* be doing to lose weight; where they struggle is the process of changing their behaviour. In other words, a client who has been trying to lose weight over a long period of time may well be very clued up on different eating regimes and diets and know they should exercise more, but actually doing that when they are faced with all the obstacles and temptations that life throws at them is the tough bit. To a certain extent, they don't need your knowledge and most of the time they will actually have the answers themselves. They know how they tick, so asking the right questions will help to pull that information to the front. The client is their own expert. You are just enabling them to succeed.

What sort of questions should I ask?

In normal situations, we ask questions to get information for ourselves: what time is it? how did you do that? and so on. In the client–trainer relationship, the answers are more for the benefit of the client than they are for you. If you ask the right questions, your clients will gain deeper understanding through their own responses and find their own answers to the behavioural problems they experience. Open questions that do not elicit a 'yes' or 'no' response are best in this situation and will help the client to continue their enquiries. For example:

Trainer: How have you got on since last week?
Client: I wanted to get to the gym three times in between our sessions, but I only managed to go once.
Trainer: Why was that?
Client: Well, life just kind of took over. I had planned to go on Monday night,

but I was exhausted when I got in and my son wasn't feeling well, so I stayed in to look after him and it just kind of went downhill from there

Trainer: Couldn't you have gone later in the week?

Client: Yes, but by that time I felt it wasn't worth it.

Trainer: What stopped you from going?

Client: I felt like a failure and it was just easier to do what I always do.

Trainer: Let's go back to your original goal. You want exercise to be a regular part of your life and have more energy?

Client: Right.

Trainer: What has stopped you doing that in the past?

Client: Life. I always seem too busy. That's why I hired you!

Trainer: OK. I see you once a week, so I can't do everything for you. What could you have done differently this week to get you away from what you have always done?

Client: I could've not given up on Monday. I could have reminded myself of my commitment and re-planned my week.

Trainer: How could you have reminded yourself of your commitment?

Client: I could put my exercise schedule with the days I plan to exercise on the fridge.

Trainer: OK, and what else?

Client: I could ask my partner to support me more. He could have looked after our son on Monday, but I didn't even ask and he didn't offer.

(and so on).

In this example, the client is coming up with their own ideas and seeing where they have gone wrong before and what they could do to change things in the future, rather than the personal trainer prescribing what they need to do. This is a far more effective way of motivating your clients.

Knowing the nuts and bolts, the technical side of your business, is obviously critical and this must be the linchpin of everything else you do. However, you must also take time to focus on the psychology. You are dealing with human beings in your work. For all their physical hopes, dreams and desires, you cannot ignore what is going on in the mind. We are, after all, holistic beings and you cannot separate the mind from the body. This chapter should have given you some insight into some different theories and ideas that might help shape the way you work with your clients and manage your relationship with them in the long term.

APPENDIX 1
SAMPLE FORMS

Over the following pages you will find a number of forms that you can use with your clients. Feel free to use them as they are or alter them to suit your needs. You may prefer to condense some information so that new clients don't have to fill in so many forms. Remember that some of your clients will find it very motivating to record what they do and to track themselves along their fitness journey. However, some will find this process tedious, so always tailor your use of such forms and lists carefully.

There are also a number of forms that are designed for you to use in your business.

Welcome letter

(Your name or company name)
(Your contact details)

(Date)

Dear__________

Welcome to personal training! I enjoyed meeting you last week and would like to commend you on your commitment to a healthier lifestyle. I am also delighted that you have chosen me as your trainer. Thank you!

Your welcome pack contains the following:

- Health Questionnaire
- Client Details Form
- Fitness Goals
- Terms and Conditions
- Invoice
- My profile
- An information article about getting started in exercise
- And a small gift to help you get motivated!

If you have the time, please fill in the first four forms on the list before our first session next week. This will enable us to get started straight away. Please also bring your diary so we can schedule your appointments for the month and your first payment of __________.

Your first session is on __________ *(date)* at __________ *(time)* and will take place at __________ *(location of session).*

If you have any questions in the meantime, do get in touch. My contact details are at the top of this letter.

I look forward to seeing you on __________*(day of first session).*

Kind regards

(Your name)

Health questionnaire

For most people, taking part in a programme of physical activity is perfectly safe. However, for a small number, it may be necessary to check with your doctor before embarking on a new fitness regime. For this reason, please fill in the questionnaire below. Please answer each question honestly and speak to me if you are unsure about any of the questions.

Name: ______________________________

Have you ever had any of the following? If yes, please provide full details overleaf.

Heart trouble or chest pain Y/N

Balance problems Y/N

High blood pressure Y/N

Hay fever/sinus problems Y/N

Asthma Y/N

Arthritis/osteoarthritis Y/N

Sports injury Y/N

Muscular aches and pains Y/N

Back problems Y/N

Are you pregnant? Y/N

Do you know of any other reason why you should not take part in a physical activity programme?

Please list any prescribed medication you are currently taking:

I understand that it is my responsibility to inform *(your business name)* of any medical condition I have that may affect my ability to exercise and to update this information as necessary. I will not hold *(your business name)* liable in any way for injuries that occur while I am training.

Signed ____________________________ Date ____________

Client details form

Name: ______________________________ Date of birth: ___________

Address: ______________________________________

____

____

Phone: Home: __________________

Mobile: __________________

Work: __________________

Email: ______________________________

Occupation: __________________________

Next of kin: Name: ______________________________

Relationship to you: _______________________

Address: ______________________________

____

____

Phone: Home: ____________________

Mobile: ____________________

Work: ____________________

Fitness goals

Name:

What would you like to achieve? Circle those that apply:

Improve muscle tone	Improve cardiovascular fitness
Stress management	Sports conditioning
Rehabilitiation	Reshape body
Reduce muscular tension	Increase flexibility
Achieve optimal health	Weight loss
Weight gain	Gain strength

Other ____

When would you like to achieve these goals?

Why are these goals important to you?

How long have you been thinking about these goals?

Does your partner support you in your efforts to be more fit and healthy?

If you have tried in the past to achieve these goals, what stopped you from succeeding?

On a scale of 1–10, how important is it that you achieve your goals?

Goals log

Name

	Goal	*Benefits*	*Actions*	*Time frame*	*Success indicators*
1					
2					
3					
4					
5					
6					

Follow up date:

Daily record

Date: ___________

Exercise (record what you did, how long you spent doing it and how hard you worked):

____

____

____

Diet			
Time	*Food*	*Where were you?*	*Feelings*

How many glasses of water have you had today?

How many portions of fruit and vegetables have you had today?

How much alcohol have you had today?

What was your general mood today?

Did you achieve your main goal today?

What is your main goal tomorrow?

(NB: these last two questions could be about anything, not just health and fitness.)

Terms and conditions

1. Sessions will be for one hour. If you are late for a session, this time will be deducted from your session. If I am late for a session, this time will be made up at a mutually convenient time, but not necessarily during that specific session.
2. Every effort will be made to offer regular session times should these be required, but this cannot be guaranteed. Bookings can be made up to two months in advance.
3. Payment. My personal training fee is ______ per session. Payment is due in advance of regular sessions. If you are training on this basis, payment will be due monthly on the 1st of each calendar month. An invoice will be given to you on your last session of the previous month. For ad hoc training, payment will be due on the day. Cheques should be made payable to ______________.
4. Your session fees include the one-hour training session plus ______________ *(this might incorporate added extras depending on the level of service clients have purchased or as a bonus to all clients, such as email contact between sessions, phone support as needed between sessions, dietary evaluation, etc.).*
5. Changes to session times. For regular clients, please give me 24 hours' notice if you need to re-schedule a session. Re-arrangement will only be offered for up to one session per calendar month. Any extra changes will result in you losing those sessions. If less than 24 hours' notice is given of cancellation, you will forfeit that session. For ad hoc clients, payment will be due for sessions cancelled with less than 24 hours' notice. No further sessions will be offered until this payment is made.
6. You will be required to keep ______________ *(your business name)* informed of any changes to your medical condition that may affect your exercise programme and it is also your responsibility to let your trainer know of any change of address or contact number.
7. Correct footwear will be required at all training sessions

I have read, understood and agree to the conditions listed above.

Name: ________________________________

Signed: ________________________________

Date: ________________________________

Doctor's consent

To: ____________________________ *(Your company name)*

(Your company address)

____________________________ *(client's name)* has informed me that they wish to take part in a programme of progressive exercise. This may include, but not be restricted to, resistance and cardiovascular training. I see no reason why this person should not participate.

Signed: ____________________________

Print name: ____________________________

Date: ____________________________

Phone number: ____________________________

Please identify any recommendations, exercise restrictions or extra information that may be appropriate for your patient:

____

____

____

____

Invoice

(Your company name)

(Company address)

To: ______________________ *(Client's name – company or person)*

(Client's address)

Invoice number:

Date:

Service of Personal Training for the month of: ________________________

Date	Time	Amount
	Total now due:	

Cheques should be made payable to: ______________________________

Prospective client presentation checklist

Before you meet a prospective client, it can be useful to have a checklist so that you make sure you have everything you need for the meeting. This will make you feel in control, prepared and more likely to get the business.

Take the following:

- Portfolio of qualifications
- Menu of all the services you offer
- Pens
- Appointment diary
- New starter pack containing:
    - Terms and conditions
    - Welcome letter
    - Business card
    - Personal profile – limit this to one side of A4
    - Relevant fitness information – an added bonus
    - Health screening form
    - Copies of relevant published articles by you
    - Any other freebies you would like to offer. Remember, if someone is paying out for something as intangible as personal training, it is good to give them something physical to go away with.

Client retention checklist

With the best intentions in the world, it is still easy to let standards slip. While you may start off intending to offer exceptional service to your clients and do everything you can to make your clients feel special and add extra value, without a systemised approach you can get too busy to do those 'extras' that make all the difference.

Below is a list of strategies and added extras to help you keep your clients in the long term.

- Keep your sessions purely professional and focused on the business of training.
- Be on time, every time, and always do what you say you are going to do.
- Have a written agreement so that clients are signed up a month in advance.
- Send birthday and Christmas (or other religious holiday) cards. Send postcards while your client is on holiday. Imagine their surprise when they arrive at their hotel and there is a card from you!
- Reinforce your positive intentions for your client regularly.
- Send/give rewards (small gift items) as appropriate, i.e. on achieving goals, when your client needs extra support, etc.
- Be absolutely clear and fair in all your business communication. This means billing on time and expecting payment on the agreed terms and conditions every time. Be assertive!
- Under-promise and over-deliver.
- Have a full client list. If you have a waiting list that is even better.
- Invite your clients to social and special events exclusive to your clients.
- Send out a regular newsletter to keep your clients in touch and make them feel as though they are part of an exclusive 'club' and that they are getting more for their money.
- Encourage your clients to set challenging goals and help them achieve them.

Risk assessment

(Company name)

Activity and location	Significant hazards	Who may be at risk from these hazards?	Extent of risk	List existing controls for risk	Measures to be taken in uncontrolled risk	Action by whom and date to be completed

Assessment carried out by: ______________________

Date: ______________________

Review date: ______________________

APPENDIX 2 USEFUL ADDRESSES

Professional bodies

National Register of Personal Trainers
PO Box 314
Chalfont St Peter
Buckinghamshire
SL9 9ZL
tel: 0870 200 6010
website: www.nrpt.co.uk

Fitness Professionals Ltd
Kalbarri House
107–113 London Road
London
E13 0DA
tel: 08705 133 434
website: www.fitpro.com

Register of Exercise Professionals (REPs)
8–10 Crown Hill
Croydon
Surrey
CR0 1RZ
tel: 020 8686 6464
website: www.exerciseregister.org
email: info@exerciseregister.org

PT Plus UK
107–113 London Road
London
E13 0DA
tel: 020 8821 9002
website: www.ptplus.co.uk
email: info@ptplus.co.uk

Training providers

This is by no means a comprehensive list. Contact REPs (see above) for up-to-date information regarding current training courses recognised by them.

Focus Training
Focus Training Headquarters
5 Canon Court
Institute Street
Bolton
Lancashire
BL1 1PZ
tel: 0800 731 9781 or 01204 388330
website: www.focus-training.com

CK Academy
Sparrows Herne
Kingswood
Basildon
Essex
SS16 5JP
tel: 01268 522954 or 01268 522255
www.ckacademy.co.uk
email: info@ckacademy.co.uk

Lifetime
3 Berkeley Square
Bristol
BS8 1HL
tel: 0117 9078200
website: www.lifetimehf.co.uk

Premier Training International
Premier House
Willowside Park
Canal Road
Trowbridge
Wiltshire
BA14 8RH
tel: 01225 353535
website: www.premierglobal.co.uk
email: enquiries@premierglobal.co.uk

YMCA Fitness Industry Training
111 Great Russell Street
London
WC1B 3NP
tel: 020 7343 1850
website: www.ymcafit.org.uk
email: info@ymcafit.org.uk

Sports Coach UK
114 Cardigan Road
Headingley
Leeds
LS6 3BJ
tel: 0113 2744802
website: www.sportscoachuk.org
email: coaching@sportscoachuk.org

The Wright Foundation
PO Box 159
Dundee
DD1 9HF
tel: 01382 451146
website: www.wrightfoundation.com
email: info@wrightfoundation.com

St John Ambulance
27 St John's Lane
London
EC1M 4BU
tel: 08700 104950
website: www.sja.org.uk

British Red Cross
tel: 0870 1709110 (England, Scotland and Wales) or 028 9033 1555 (NI and Isle of Man)
website: www.redcrossfirstaidtraining.co.uk

British Association of Cardiac Rehab.
Town Hall Exchange
Castle Street
Farnham
Surrey
GU9 7ND
tel: 01252 720640
website: www.bacrphaseiv.co.uk

Insurance

CMC Insurance Consultants
tel: 01794 516740
This company specialises in insurance to the fitness industry.

Money

Try the following companies for computer programs that help you to manage your finances:

Quickbooks
tel: 0845 6062161
website: www.quickbooks.co.uk

Sage
tel: 0845 2450295
website: www.sage.co.uk

Networking organisations

Magenta Circle
Magenta House
40 Tudor Gardens
Stony Stratford
Milton Keynes
MK11 1HX
website: www.magentacircle.co.uk

Business Network International (BNI)
website: www.bni-europe.com
email: bniuk@eurobni.com

Business Referral Exchange
18 Pine Grove
Bookmans Park
Herts
AL9 7BS
tel: 0845 100 4822
website: www.brenet.co.uk

Personal safety

The Suzy Lamplugh Trust
PO Box 17818
London
SW14 8WW
tel: 020 8876 0305
website: www.suzylamplugh.org
email: info@suzylamplugh.org
The Suzy Lamplugh Trust, a registered charity, is the leading authority on personal safety. Its role is to minimise the damage caused to individuals and to society by aggression in all its forms – physical, verbal and psychological.

Risk assessment

The Health and Safety Executive (HSE) has information on this subject, much of it available free.
HSE Books
PO Box 1999
Sudbury, Suffolk
CO10 2WA
tel: 01787 881165
website: www.hsebooks.co.uk or www.hse.gov.uk

Special populations

Older people:

British Heart Foundation's National Centre for Physical Activity and Health
Loughborough University
Loughborough
Leicestershire
LE11 3TU
tel: 01509 223259
website: www.bhfactive.org.uk
email: bhfactive@lists.lboro.ac.uk

International Council for Active Ageing
website: www.icaa.cc

International Society for Ageing and Physical Activity
website: www.isapa.org

REFERENCES AND FURTHER READING

American College of Obstetricians and Gynaecologists (ACOG) Committee (2002), 'Opinion no. 267: Exercise during pregnancy and the post-partum period', *Obstetrics and Gynecology*, 2002:99, pp. 171–3

American College of Obstetricians and Gynaecologists (ACOG) Committee (1994), 'Technical Bulletin Number 189: Exercise during pregnancy and the post-partum period', *International Journal of Gynaecology and Obstetrics* 1994:45(1), pp. 65–70

American College of Sports Medicine (2005), *Guidelines for Exercise Testing and Prescription*, Lippincott, Williams and Wilkins

American College of Sports Medicine (2000), *Current Comment: Exercise and the Older Adult*

American College of Sports Medicine (2000), *Current Comment: Exercise During Pregnancy*

American College of Sports Medicine (1998), 'Position Stand: Exercise and physical activity for older adults', *Medicine and science in sports and exercise*, 1998:30(6), pp. 992–1008

American College of Sports Medicine (1997), *Exercise Management for Persons with Chronic Diseases and Disabilities*, Human Kinetics

American College of Sports Medicine and American Diabetes Association Joint Position Stand (1997), 'Diabetes mellitus and exercise', *Medicine and Science in Sports and Exercise*, 28(12) pp. i–vi

Anderson, K. and Zemke, R. (2002), *Delivering Knock-your-socks-off Service*, Amacom

Bean, A. (2005), *The Complete Guide to Strength Training*, A & C Black

Bell, C. R. and Zemke, R. (1989), *Service Wisdom: Creating and Maintaining the Customer Service Edge*, Lakewood Publications

Biddle, S., Fox, K., Boutcher, S. and Faulkner, G. (2000), *Physical Activity and Psychological Well-being*, Routledge

Blanchard, K. and Bowles, S. (1998), *Raving Fans*, HarperCollins

Borg, G. (1982), 'A category scale with ratio properties for intermodal and interindividual comparisons' in Geissler, H. G. and Petzoid, P. (eds) (1982), *Psychophysical Judgement and the Process of Perception*, VEB Deutscher Verlag der Wissenschaften, Berlin

Borg, G. A. (1973), 'Perceived exertion: a note on history and methods', *Medicine and Science in Sports and Exercise*, 5, pp. 90–3

British Medical Association (2004), *The British Medical Association's New Guide to Medicines and Drugs*, Dorling Kindersley

British National Formulary, Biannual, *Reference of classified notes on clinical conditions, drugs and preparations for practitioners*

Brown, R. (2005), *The Networking Bible*, self-published, available at www.rob-brown.com

Buzan, T. (2002), *How to Mind Map: The Ultimate Thinking Tool That Will Change Your Life*, HarperCollins, London

Carlzon, J. (1989), *Moments of Truth*, HarperCollins, New York

Covey, S. R. (1999), *The Seven Habits of Highly Effective People*, Simon and Schuster

Department of Health (2004), *At Least 5 a Week: Evidence on the Impact of Physical Activity and its Relationship to Health*

Department of Health (April 2001), *Exercise Referral Systems: A National Quality Assurance Framework*

Dick, F. W. (2003), *Sports Training Principles*, A & C Black

DiFiore, J. (2003), *The Complete Guide to Postnatal Fitness*, A & C Black

Emmett, R. (2001), *The Procrastinator's Handbook – mastering the art of doing it now*, Fusion Press

Fleck, S. J. and Kraemer, W. J. (1997), *Designing Resistance Training Programs*, Human Kinetics, Champaign, IL

Ford, B. (2002), *High Energy Habits*, Pocket Books

Forster, H. (2002), *Dejunk Your Life*, Aurum Press Ltd

Forster, M. (2000), *Get Everything Done and Still Have Time To Play*, Help Yourself

Gerber, M. E. (1995), *The E-Myth Revisited*, HarperCollins, London

Goliszek, A. PhD (1993), *60 Second Stress Management*, Bantam Books

Health and Safety Executive (1999), *5 Steps to Risk Assessment*

Janz, N. K. and Becker, M. H. (1984), 'The health belief model: a decade later', *Health Education Quarterly*, 11(1), 1–47

Kraemer, W. J. (1998), 'Periodization in Resistance Training', *IDEA Personal Trainer*, 9, 27–34

Kraemer, W. J., Fleck, S. J. and Evans, W. J. (1996), 'Strength and power training: physiological mechanisms of adaptation', *Exercise and Sports Science Reviews*, 24, pp. 363–97

Lawrence, D. (2005), *The Complete Guide to Exercising Away Stress*, A & C Black

Lazarus, R. S. (1966), *Psychological Stress and the Coping Process*, McGraw-Hill, New York

Locke, E. A., Shaw, K. N., Saari, L. M. and Latham, G.P. (1981), 'Goal setting and task performance: 1969–1980', *Psychological Bulletin*, 90(1), pp. 125–52

Loehr, J. and Schwartz, T. (2005), *The Power of Full Engagement*, Free Press, Simon and Schuster

Lundin, S. C., Paul, H. and Christensen, J. (2000), *FISH!*, Hyperion

Marcus, B. H. and Forsyth, L. H. (2003), *Motivating People to be Physically Active*, Human Kinetics

Matvayev, L. P. (1966), *Periodisation of Sports Training*, Fiskultura I Sport

McArdle, W. D., Katch, F. I. and Katch, V. I. (1996), *Exercise Physiology: Energy, Nutrition and Human Performance (4th edition)*, Lippincott Williams and Wilkins

Mehrabian, A. (1981), *Silent Messages: Implicit Communication of Emotions and Attitudes*, Wadsworth

Morris, S. and Smith, J. (1998), *Understanding Mind Maps in a Week*, Hodder and Stoughton, London

Orr, R., 'Periodized Programs Part 1', PT on the net: www.ptonthenet.com

Presbie, R. J. and Brown, P. L (1977), *Physical Education: The Behavior Modification Approach*, National Education Association, Washington, DC

Prochaska, J. O. and DiClemente, C. C. (1983), 'The stages and processes of self-change in smoking: towards an integrative model of change' *Journal of Consulting and Clinical Psychology*, 51 390–5

Rauscher, F. H., Shaw, G. L. and Ky, K. N. (1993), 'The Mozart Effect', *Nature*, Vol. 365, p. 611

Robbins, A. (2001), *Unlimited Power*, Pocket Books

Rochlitz, S. (1993), *Why Do Music Conductors Live into Their 90s? The Simple, Revolutionary Discovery That Can Make You Live Longer, Increase Your Stamina and Stretch*, Human Ecology Balancing Sciences

Roitman, J. L., Kelsey, M., LaFontaine, T. P., Southard, D. R., Williams, M. A. and York, T. (1998), *ACSM's Resource Manual for Guidelines for Exercise Testing and Prescription, (3rd edition)*, Williams and Wilkins, Baltimore

Rosenstock, I. M. (1974), 'The health belief model and preventative health behaviour', *Health Education Monographs*, 2 (4), 355–87

Sarafino, E. P. (2005), *Health Psychology – Biopsychosocial Interactions*, John Wiley and Sons

Skinner, B. F. (1953), *Science and Human Behavior*, Free Press, New York

Sonstroem, R. J. (1988), 'Psychological models' in Dishman, R. K. (1988), *Exercise Adherence: its Impact on Public Health*, Human Kinetics, Champaign, IL

Soukup, J. T., Maynard, T. S. and Kovaleski, J. E. (1994), 'Resistance training guidelines for individuals with diabetes mellitus', *The diabetic educator* (20) pp. 129–37

Spirduso, W. W. (1995), *Physical Dimensions of Aging*, Human Kinetics

Steinmetz, J., Blankenship, J., Brown, L., Hall, D. and Miller, G. (1980), *Managing Stress Before it Manages You*, Bull Publishing Company

White House Office of Consumer Affairs (1990), *Small Business Success*, Vol. III

Willis, J. D. and Campbell, L. F. (1992), *Exercise Psychology*, Human Kinetics

Wilmore, J. H. and Costill, D. L (2004), *Physiology of Sport and Exercise (3rd edition)*, Human Kinetics, Champaign, IL

Wolf, L. A., Hall, P., Webb, K. A., Goodman, L., Monga, M. and McGrath, M. J. (1989), 'Prescription of aerobic exercise during pregnancy', *Sports Medicine*, 8, pp. 273–301

INDEX